QUANTITATIVE LITERACY
AND REASONING

Kendall Hunt
publishing company

Debra Hall
James Madison University

All graphs courtesy of Debra Hall.

Graphs on pages 77, 115, and 125 courtesy of Debra Hall using data from www.collegeresults.org.

Graphs on pages 75, 77, 83, 99, 101, 106-107, 109-110, 112-113, 115, 121-122, 124-125, 127-130, 135-137, 143-144, 152, 154, 156, 158, and 181 created using Minitab Inc. software.

Standard Normal Table in Appendix II and on pages 133 and 134 from *Statistics in Action: Understanding a World of Data*, 2/e by Ann E. Watkins, Richard L. Scheaffer and George W. Cobb. Copyright © 2008 by Key Curriculum Press. Reprinted by permission.

Cover image © Shutterstock, Inc.

Kendall Hunt
publishing company

www.kendallhunt.com
Send all inquiries to:
4050 Westmark Drive
Dubuque, IA 52004-1840

Copyright © 2018 by Debra Hall.

PAK ISBN: 978-1-5249-5228-0
Text alone ISBN: 978-1-5249-5229-7

Kendall Hunt Publishing Company has the exclusive rights to reproduce this work, to prepare derivative works from this work, to publicly distribute this work, to publicly perform this work and to publicly display this work.

All rights reserved. No part of this publication may be reproduced, stored in a retrieval system, or transmitted, in any form or by any means, electronic, mechanical, photocopying, recording, or otherwise, without the prior written permission of the copyright owner.

Published in the United States of America

CONTENTS

CHAPTER 3: LINEAR AND EXPONENTIAL EXPRESSIONS AND FUNCTIONS 57

CHAPTER 4: INTRODUCTION TO DATA AND DATA ANALYSIS 103

CHAPTER 5: USING DATA TO MAKE SENSE OF THE WORLD 169

CHAPTER 6: WORKING WITH SET AND CATEGORICAL VARIABLE RELATIONSHIPS 211

APPENDIX I: BASIC SKILLS REVIEW 243

APPENDIX II: STANDARD NORMAL TABLE 265

INDEX 269

THANK YOU!

I extend many thanks to those in the James Madison University
Department of Mathematics & Statistics who supported and encouraged this undertaking.

I am particularly thankful for the editorial support of Greg Jansen and Arlene Casiple.
Without their editorial help and input in the initial course-pack, this book would not have been possible!

–Deb Hall

INTRODUCTION

WHAT IS QUANTITATIVE LITERACY AND REASONING?

Around eight years ago, when I was asked to develop a quantitative reasoning (QR) course at James Madison University, I found myself asking this very question. I suspect that many of you asked some version of it when you first learned you needed to take this class. This course is different from the long-standing core math courses of college curriculums like Algebra, Calculus, and Introductory Statistics, which have nearly universal agreement on content. Unlike these courses, coursework in quantitative reasoning *emphasizes understanding and using quantitative data and information in a real-world context*. This approach is a relatively new topic in the college curriculum conversation. Though higher education and mathematics organizations have been calling for a shift to this type of mathematics for at least 20 years, what goes into such a course is far from settled. Even what to call "it" is up in the air with three phrases in prominent usage: Quantitative Reasoning (QR), Quantitative Literacy (QL), and Numeracy. A search for these phrases results in hundreds of thousands of hits, all with diverse views on what this "math" entails.

Several recurring themes and phrases permeate the expert perspective on what a course in Quantitative Reasoning is about. Quantitatively literate individuals are described as having "habits of the mind" to comfortably weigh quantitative evidence, to

seek out and reason with quantitative data/information, and to use simple math to understand sophisticated situations. Individuals with these "habits" incorporate them into all aspects of their personal and professional lives in the formulation of complex arguments which they then communicate in various forms including words, tables, and graphs. Such habits are second nature to some, but for most people development of these "habits" requires guidance, opportunity, and ongoing practice in a variety of settings. Should you wish to learn more, here are some of the best and leading resources:

- ➢ The Mathematical Association of America has called for coursework in Quantitative Reasoning/Literacy for over 20 years. You can find many resources at the MAA website, including several extensive reports at https://www.maa.org/programs-and-communities/curriculum-resources/survey-and-reports. You can also go to the MAA website and search on "reports" to find the Survey and Reports section.
- ➢ Carleton College was one of the first institutions to make Quantitative Reasoning a priority through their ongoing, campus-wide initiative that crosses all disciplines, called *Quantitative Inquiry, Reasoning, and Knowledge (QuIRK) https://apps.carleton.edu/quirk/about/. Ten Foundational Quantitative Reasoning Questions https://apps.carleton.edu/quirk/curricular/10questions/ is especially useful.*
- ➢ The National Numeracy Network (NNN) is the organization of primarily educational institutions and faculty in the United States dedicated to this field of mathematics. http://serc.carleton.edu/nnn/about/index.html
- ➢ The Association of American Colleges and Universities (AACU) has long supported greater emphasis on the understanding and use of quantitative information. Their definition can be found here: https://www.aacu.org/value/rubrics/quantitative-literacy. Their summer 2014 edition of *peerReview* was dedicated to Quantitative Reasoning (https://www.aacu.org/peerreview/2014/summer).

The resources mentioned above, along with many others, helped to shape this book. Each of the descriptions show a clear connection between quantitative skills and the ability to apply and communicate about them in real-life context. Clearly, a course that uses this book is not a traditional number crunching math class; there are large sections of material where there are essentially no calculations at all. In nearly all parts of this material, getting the correct numerical result is just the beginning of the work to be completed, not the end. Though there are formulas and calculations, a course that uses this textbook focuses more broadly on careful reading, analysis, critical thinking, decision-making, and contextual communication. All of the presented activities are designed to help you further develop those Quantitative Reasoning skills and aptitudes described. You will have many opportunities to practice basic mathematics, literacy, reasoning skills, critically analyze arguments and quantitative information about many real-life topics, and communicate numerical findings in a real-world context. *Quantitative Literacy and Reasoning* is about preparing you for life as an active, well-educated citizen of the world we live in—a world filled with seemingly limitless information, much of which is useless noise. It is about facing, possibly embracing, the quantitative information that permeates the modern world and doing so with confidence that you will be able to think about that information with enough critical insight to be aware that such information needs to be questioned for its potential biases, questionable sources, and cherry-picked data. You need to recognize when others misinterpret or misapply results, so that you are not among those led to wrong decisions. Throughout your life, you will need to understand and use quantitative information to make financial and health-related decisions, to make solid professional decisions, to decide who you want your leaders to be, and even to understand how others are using information to make decisions that affect you and society. Though most people's lives rarely require them to complete complex calculations, exceptionally few of us have days devoid of quantitative information that impact our decisions.

IMPORTANCE OF MEANINGFUL COMMUNICATION

Meaningful communication of quantitative information to a general audience is a challenge for most people, including experts in quantitative and communication fields. And if they are struggling to communicate the quantitative information, it is likely that their audience is struggling to understand them. It is not that this type of communication is so very difficult, but rather that it has not been part of traditional education. *Meaningful communication about quantitative information is one of the most critical expectations* of the book. This communication is challenging for most students initially, not because the interpretations are particularly difficult to write, but because writing them is unfamiliar and requires a level of specificity beyond what we use in everyday "texting" and bullet-type communication. The interpretation statements are very specific and structured, so much in fact, that many students see them as straightforward and thus never practice writing them. That lack of practice later creates less than satisfactory results in the graded work. *You must practice writing the interpretations to become comfortable and confident with writing them, don't try to memorize them right before an exam! The communication and interpretation expectations are as, and often more, important than the calculations!*

You will be asked to write interpretations that meaningfully stand on their own and that any <u>reasonably-educated, general audience member</u> should be able to understand. Such communication requires some attention to context and a willingness to write slightly more detail than is perhaps typical for you. Things to ponder as you write for your audience:

➢ Consider the quantitative information that you hear or read in classes or everyday life. How often are you provided with a clearly stated mathematical question(s) before the quantitative information is provided? Outside of examples meant to show/teach calculations in a course, how often is the quantitative information provided with or conveyed in calculation form? Of course, in real life the answer to both questions is almost NEVER.

➢ Think about times when you have read or heard something in the media or in class and then used it yourself in later discussion. Did you ever just quote the information but not really fully understand when or where the numbers came from, or who the numbers really applied to or under what conditions the information was gathered? What about the last time you were required to include quantitative information from a reliable source in a class paper or presentation, did you really understand what those "numbers" meant or did you just find numbers to meet the stated requirement, make sure you reported them and really have no idea what you were reporting? *If asked, could you have explained—in a straightforward, no technical jargon way— exactly what those numbers were telling you/us about the situation you were discussing?*

The legitimate quantitative information, (*numbers not simply pulled from the air or manipulated to produce a specific outcome*), relayed in mainstream media, textbooks, nonfield-specific journals, political discourse, and our daily lives is about the "results" of calculations. The ONLY way someone can understand the initial question and the applied meaning of the numbers is through the use of self-contained, complete, and contextual communication. Get in the habit of asking yourself, *"Does this explanation/interpretation make sense if it is all the information available to the reader?"* before moving on to the next item. Remember that since we will always focus on communication with general audiences and not some specialized group of quantitative experts, you must avoid the use of technical or mathematical terminology, except in the rare instances when there is absolutely no other choice. By learning to communicate quantitative information accurately and effectively, you will also be learning how to make sense of the quantitative information that you hear or read and recognize errors and omissions in that information.

No one is expected to have full knowledge of all topics and fields; BUT you are expected to be able to access information that would allow you to respond to unfamiliar contexts in a reasonable way. **Read carefully to be sure you understand the context and, when you encounter unfamiliar terms and situations, use the internet to look them up**! Remember Quantitative Literacy and Reasoning is about looking at the world through a lens that considers quantitative evidence and context, so we will be looking at a variety of contexts within that world and some will be unfamiliar to each of us! Do not expect each problem to spell out all contextual details; quantitative literacy requires a broad worldview and this book challenges you to seek out any necessary details that you do not already possess.

Before closing, I want to be certain that you recognize that any course using a book like this cannot be approached like just another math class. Even if you are good in math, success will not be achieved through sitting down once or twice a week for an hour to do a few calculations; calculations are a part of the expectations, but they are not the focus. Success is very attainable. In fact, many of those that consider themselves "bad" at math or "math anxious" have been shocked by their level of success. But the material requires regular work several times each week and lots of reading, writing, and practice.

The general rule of thumb for out of class college work is that students need to spend at least 2–3 hours outside of class for each credit hour, EVERY single week. Though the applicability of that rule of thumb is questioned in some settings, it genuinely applies to learning this type of material. That means that in a 3-credit hour course, you need to spend 6–9 hours of focused out-of-class time each week. Spread those hours throughout the week with at least 30–45 minutes of review time within a few hours after each class session to fine tune your notes from class. When big assignments or exams are planned, more time is needed! Do not allow yourself to get behind! Build regularly scheduled study and practice time into your schedule!

I hope you have a great semester!

Debra Hall

NOTES ON ROUNDING AND REQUIRED NUMBER OF DECIMAL PLACES IN THIS BOOK

Determining the number of decimal places to keep in recording final answers is a concern that crops up repeatedly in classes where calculations are necessary. Occasionally, rounding expectations will be spelled out as part of the problem itself and, when specified, follow that guidance. Otherwise, the following standards for rounding are used in this book and are not restated in every problem.

➢ Except when specified otherwise, we round and record final decimal answers to the nearest ten-thousandth and, when the response is to be written in percentage form, that recorded answer is reported to the nearest hundredth. (The book does not use the significant digit approach.)

➢ In the situation where the decimal form has no digits other than 0 until beyond that the ten- thousandth position, do not round to 0. Give enough digits to see the first nonzero value.

➢ Remember that rounding must only be used in the last step of recording the answer. In multistep calculations, rounding between steps will introduce errors that will make most final answers incorrect! The best way to minimize the chance of such errors is, whenever possible, to enter entire calculation expressions into your calculator in one step! This is easy to do on most scientific and graphing calculators if you make use of parentheses and order of operations!

➢ When rounding to the nearest ten-thousandth place, you need to see at least the hundred-thousandth place. If that place is a digit of 5 or higher, then the ten-thousandth place digit will be rounded up.

A NOTE ON COLOR CODING IN THIS BOOK

Throughout the book, student response examples are colored blue to indicate an acceptable student response for problems. Students are expected to use these as basis for writing their own responses to similar problems in the Your Turns and exercises. Additionally, hints for student success in this class are colored red.

CHAPTER 1
Units of Measurement and Dimensional Analysis

CHAPTER OBJECTIVES

Upon completion of this chapter, the student should be able to

❑ Identify and correctly express all given factors given in a quantitative scenario involving units of measure, then determine which acceptable conversion factors are needed.

❑ Construct the proper product expression of given factors and conversion factors using that expression to calculate and express the numerical result with the required units of measure.

❑ Write a complete contextual and self-contained response to the quantitative question, assuming no prior reader knowledge of the question or calculation.

Let us begin our work with units of measure and dimensional analysis with a few rules about the use of abbreviations.

- Many, but not all, units of measure have standard abbreviations.

- In work associated with the text, only the unit of measure abbreviations provided in the text are acceptable.

- Never use non-standard abbreviations, even when that means the entire unit of measure must be completely written out.

- Unit of measure abbreviations are generally acceptable in tables of values or calculations.

- Abbreviations are NOT generally acceptable in sentences. The dollar sign symbol, $, is an exception.

As you read each section in this and future chapters, get in the habit of completing the Your Turn problems immediately after working through the associated example. This reinforces what you have just read and helps you develop the confidence that you understand the material presented in the example and are able to apply what you learned. If you find that you cannot yet work the Your Turn, you will know to seek help on the specific concept from your instructor or other resource right away so that you do not get behind.

Be sure your responses are reported in ordinary form except when scientific notation or forms with base 10 multipliers are specified.

Don't forget the rounding rules and required number of decimal places discussed immediately before this chapter!

1.1 UNITS OF MEASUREMENT

A big part of "context" when working with numerical information in real-world contexts is the "units of measurement" involved.

YOUR TURN 1: To get a couple of good working definitions of unit, follow these directions:

➢ Go to http://www.thefreedictionary.com. At this page you will find definitions from several reputable dictionaries. (The specific source dictionary is identified in the CITE information below each block of definitions.)
➢ Type the term "**unit**" in the search box.
➢ Record the two designated definitions from *American Heritage® Dictionary of the English Language* in this space:

Definition 4:

Definition 8a:

> Record the fifth definition from *Random House Kernerman Webster's College Dictionary* in this space:

In this chapter, you will work with a variety of units for time, length, area, volume, and so forth, for both the US Customary Unit System and the Metric System. The unit equivalents that are used in examples and needed to work the Your Turns and the chapter exercises are listed in the table below. These are the only acceptable unit equivalents for the work in this text. Do not make the mistake of using different equivalents that you find listed online. *Be sure to find out from your instructor which of unit equivalents you are expected to memorize*!

Unit Equivalents for Chapter 1	
Units of Time	
1 year (yr) = 365 days (d)	1 week = 7 days
1 day = 24 hours (h)	1 hour = 60 minutes (min)
1 minute = 60 seconds (s)	1 year ≈ 52 weeks (only used if indicated in problem because of increased errors in solutions!)

Units of Length	
1 mile (mi) = 5,280 feet (ft)	1 mile = 1,760 yards (yd)
1 foot = 12 inches	1 yard = 3 feet
1 inch (in) = 0.0254 meter (m)	1 inch = 2.54 centimeter (cm)
1 foot = 30.48 centimeter	1 foot = 0.3048 meter
1 yard = 0.9144 meter	1 kilometer (km) = 0.621 mile
1 kilometer = 1,000 meter	

Miscellaneous Units	
1 kilowatt (kW) = 1,000 watt (W)	1 pound (lb) ≈ 0.4536 kilogram (kg)
1 teaspoon (tsp) = 5 milliliter (mL)	$1.00 = 100¢

1.2 DIMENSIONAL ANALYSIS

Dimensional Analysis is a multiplication process by which we can express quantitative information from one or more factors with a given set of units in an equivalent quantitative form with different units. *NOTE the use of the word "process."* It is the process that moves us from one form to the other that is most important throughout this material, not just the final numeric answer. There are lots of short cuts and alternative methods to arrive at the final numeric answer, but they are not acceptable substitutions for the dimensional analysis process presented in this chapter. Though you may be tempted to simply "punch in" numbers on your calculator and then attach the required units at the end, DON'T do it! Only units of measure that first appear in your complete product expression are available to appear in the final numerical answer.

As you will see in the examples, dimensional analysis involves translating the quantitative information from the problem into a single numerical expression made up of problem-provided **given factors** and the unit equivalent **conversion factors** needed to arrive at the numerical result in the form specified in the problem. *Factors* are the quantities (including the stated units) being multiplied. *Numerical expressions* are combinations of numbers, symbols, and operators that express the value of something. Unlike equations, expressions are one sided and have no equal sign until they are evaluated.

As you will see in the examples that follow, dimensional analysis takes advantage of the fact that multiplication by factors that are equivalent to 1 does not change the value(s) of the factor(s) given in the problem; they only change the form. Each problem will be completed by first listing each of the factors given in the problem and then multiplying by the unit conversion factors necessary to go from the units initially provided in the problem to the units specified for the response. Once the appropriate units in the expression are cancelled, you are ready to find the final numerical answer by using your calculator; just be sure to bring over the remaining units from the expression into your answer. Remember, that the only way a unit is available to appear in the answer is if it appeared and was not cancelled in the expression.

Before beginning the examples, consider the well-known equivalent units of time: **1 year = 365 days**, (assuming a nonleap year). Note that each of the unit equivalent pairs shown in the earlier table of unit equivalents could be expressed in three equivalent forms, as illustrated below. The second and third forms are the <u>unit</u> conversion forms (they are the forms equivalent to 1).

$$1 \text{ year} = 365 \text{ days} \qquad \frac{1 \text{ year}}{365 \text{ days}} = 1 \qquad \frac{365 \text{ days}}{1 \text{ year}} = 1$$

EXAMPLE 1: Express 2 days in seconds.

$$\mathbf{2 \text{ days}} \times \frac{24 \text{ hours}}{1 \text{ day}} \times \frac{60 \text{ minutes}}{1 \text{ hour}} \times \frac{60 \text{ seconds}}{1 \text{ minute}} = 172,800 \text{ seconds}$$

The solution has four factors. Only the first factor was provided in the problem. The other three factors are unit conversion forms of equivalent units of time. Note that there is a logical order to the factors: day -> hours -> minutes -> seconds. Though multiplication can be performed in any order, working in logical order (from larger to smaller units) helps prevent mistakes.

In working the problems in this chapter, be sure that your numerical responses are always reported in ordinary form unless you are specifically told to leave your answer in scientific notation or base 10. In setting up the product expression, never perform arithmetic in your head, on your calculator, or on the side of your paper. All of the given and conversions factors MUST be shown in the product expression before it is evaluated to arrive at the answer. (For example, using your calculator to arrive at a single conversion factor of $\dfrac{3,600 \text{ seconds}}{1 \text{ hour}}$ for the previous problem **is NOT appropriate** for the dimensional analysis process.)

EXAMPLE 2A: According to their annual report, Walmart had about **$482 million** in sales for the **year** 2015. Based on this information, what were their sales *in dollars to the nearest cent per hour?*

We are told to find the answer in "dollars to the nearest cent (meaning two decimal places) and the term **per** indicates division," which in dimensional analysis is telling us that we are looking for a fractional mathematical solution in the form $\dfrac{\$\#.\#\#}{1 \text{ hour}}$. The first factor is from the problem and the two others are the required unit conversion factors.

$$\frac{\$482,000,000}{1 \text{ year}} \times \frac{1 \text{ year}}{365 \text{ days}} \times \frac{1 \text{ day}}{24 \text{ hours}} \approx \frac{\$55,022.83}{1 \text{ hour}}$$

Compare the second factor in *Example 1* and the third factor in *Example 2*. Note that both are a conversion factor form of 1 day = 24 hours, but the values of the numerator and denominator are switched. The <u>form of the response specified</u> in the problem determines the <u>form of the factors</u> in the multiplication expression.

Notice that this expression could also be written with million expressed as 10^6 as follows:

$$\frac{\$482 \times 10^6}{1 \text{ year}} \times \frac{1 \text{ year}}{365 \text{ days}} \times \frac{1 \text{ day}}{24 \text{ hours}} \approx \frac{\$55,022.83}{1 \text{ hour}}$$

Some find this form easier to enter on their calculators because they do not need to count all the zeros in writing the problem or on their calculator. Remember to rewrite the answer in ordinary form.

Note that neither version of the dimensional analysis calculations used the word "million" in the given factor. The word *million* cannot be used in the calculation required to arrive at the numerical result. You cannot type the word *million* into your calculator to arrive at the correct values; you must enter numerical values.

The numerical answers to the dimensional analysis expression and calculation work must be in mathematical form. But the verbal form would be used in sentences. *In this problem, the mathematical form of the answer was the* $\dfrac{\$55{,}022.83}{1 \text{ hour}}$ *seen above. The verbal form is the* **$55,022.83 per hour** *used in the sentence in Example 2B.*

Since this problem involved a contextual question, the response must have a contextual sentence response like shown on next page.

EXAMPLE 2B: Write a complete sentence conveying the full context of the problem and the response.

According to their 2015 annual report, Walmart had $482,000,000 in sales which means they had to sell approximately $55,022.83 worth of products per hour.

Remember that abbreviations are generally not used in sentences. (Exception: it is acceptable to see money expressed with symbols ($) in written work, as shown here.) Also remember that the final response to every contextual word problem must be a self-contained contextual sentence.

EXAMPLE 3: Suppose you bought a **1,500-watt** electric ceramic heater to keep your room toasty at night when it is particularly cold. The winter turned out to be particularly cold, so you ran the heater for **8 hours per day** for **one-quarter of a year**. If the power company charges **8¢ per kilowatt-hour**, what were your costs for running your heater as described in units of *dollars to the nearest cent* (no other units can remain)? Provide the mathematical expression and numerical answer. Then, provide a complete contextual sentence response to the question.

*The problem reports four pieces of quantitative information (**bolded in the problem and the expression**) which became the first four factors in the expression. Several mathematical operations are communicated:* **per** *indicates division (expressed as a fraction) and both* **of** *and* **– (dash)** *indicate multiplication.*

$$1{,}500 \text{ watt} \times \frac{8 \text{ hour}}{1 \text{ day}} \times \frac{1}{4} \text{ year} \times \frac{8\cancel{c}}{1 \text{ kilowatt - hour}} \times \frac{365 \text{ days}}{1 \text{ year}} \times \frac{1 \text{ kilowatt}}{1{,}000 \text{ watt}} \times \frac{\$1.00}{100\cancel{c}} = \$87.60$$

Look at the fifth factor of this expression; the *kilo* prefix stands for 1,000. So, **1 kilowatt = 1,000 watt**. A table of metric prefixes is found after Example 8.

Sentence response:

When electricity costs 8 cents per kilowatt-hour, running a 1,500-watt electric ceramic heater for 8 hours per day for one-quarter of a year results in estimated costs of $87.60.

One final note related to this and similar problems. If the electricity costs had been given as **$0.08 per kilowatt-hour** rather than the **8¢ per kilowatt-hour** stated here, the final unit conversion factor seen above would be omitted and the fourth factor changed, resulting in this expression:

$$1{,}500 \text{ watt} \times \frac{8 \text{ hour}}{1 \text{ day}} \times \frac{1}{4} \text{ year} \times \frac{\$0.08}{1 \text{ kilowatt - hour}} \times \frac{365 \text{ days}}{1 \text{ year}} \times \frac{1 \text{ kilowatt}}{1{,}000 \text{ watt}}$$

When evaluated, the numerical answer and sentence would remain the same as seen above.

EXAMPLE 4: Suppose that the next winter you are still using a **1,500-watt** electric ceramic heater to keep your room toasty at night when it is particularly cold. You ran the heater for **3 hours per day, 5 days a week for one-quarter of a year**. Assuming the power company charges **$0.08 per kilowatt-hour**, what were your costs for running your heater as described in units of *dollars to the nearest cent* (no other units can remain)? First, provide the mathematical expression and numerical answer. Then, provide a complete contextual sentence response to the question.

$$1{,}500 \text{ watts} \times \frac{3 \text{ hours}}{1 \text{ day}} \times \frac{5 \text{ days}}{1 \text{ week}} \times \frac{1}{4} \text{ year} \times \frac{\$0.08}{\text{kilowatt - hour}} \times \frac{1 \text{ week}}{7 \text{ days}} \times \frac{365 \text{ days}}{1 \text{ year}}$$

$$\times \frac{1 \text{ kilowatt}}{1{,}000 \text{ watts}} \approx \$23.46$$

Sentence response:

When the electricity cost is $0.08 per kilowatt-hour, running a 1,500-watt electric ceramic heater for 3 hours per day, 5 days per week for one-quarter of a year results in estimated costs of $23.46.

Before continuing your reading, complete the following.

YOUR TURN 2: Rework the problem in **Example 4** with a couple of minor changes: You are still using that 1,500-watt electric ceramic heater and running it for 3 hours per day, 5 days a week for one-quarter of year. But now we are told that the power company charges 8¢ per kilowatt-hour (notice the form). Using the 1 year ≈ 52-week conversion, what were your approximate costs for running your heater as described in units of dollars to the nearest cent (no other units can remain)?

A comparison of the calculation results using the more accurate 1 year = 365 days equivalent and the less accurate 1 year ≈ 52 weeks equivalent shows a small but real monetary difference in the costs of running the heater. You might be tempted to think that "hey it is no big deal." But if you consider that the consumer is also "consuming" power continuously from more than just their heater, over an extended time frame, the difference in costs under the two calculations is going to be meaningful on a practical level. These sorts of calculations are essentially forecasts of costs to the consumer. In budgeting, wouldn't it be better to slightly overestimate future costs than underestimate them?

Also, consider the power company's revenue in response to the electricity consumed by ALL customers. Suddenly that "small" difference in calculations across ALL consumers has very real, practical impact on their "bottom line." As they look to forecast their future revenues, they would likely want the more accurate calculation.

This next example shows a dimensional analysis approach to a type of problem that is used in many fields including medicine, sociology, political science, and so forth, to express large quantities in rates that use smaller, more easily comprehended units. This approach would also allow us to directly compare characteristics of different size populations more easily by expressing the rates of the characteristics per some common quantity.

EXAMPLE 5: In 2014, there were **32,675 motor vehicle deaths** in the United States. The US population in 2014 was about **319 million people**. What was the US motor vehicle mortality rate in units of deaths (to nearest thousandth) per 100,000 people? Include an appropriate self-contained response to the question.

$$\frac{\textbf{32,675 U.S. motor vehicle deaths}}{\textbf{319,000,000 people}} \times \frac{319,000,000 \text{ people}}{3,190 \times 100,000 \text{ people}}$$

$$= \frac{10.243 \text{ U.S. motor vehicle deaths}}{100,000 \text{ people}}$$

The first factor is the problem-provided information. This type of problem typically needs only a single unit conversion factor. Its numerator is simply the same quantity as the original denominator and its denominator introduces the quantity specified for the denominator in the final answer. The other factor (bolded) in the denominator of the unit conversion factor is the value required to make the numerator and denominator equivalent, found here by 319,000,000 ÷ 100,000.

The first denominator and second numerator will cancel. The 100,000 people carries over to the answer, so no other arithmetic is performed with it, and the numerical value in the numerator of the answer is found by 32,675 ÷ 3,190 and rounded as indicated.

An acceptable alternative expression:

$$\frac{\textbf{32,675 U.S. motor vehicle deaths}}{\textbf{319} \times \textbf{10}^{\textbf{6}} \textbf{ people}} \times \frac{319 \times 10^6 \text{ people}}{3,190 \times 100,000 \text{ people}}$$

$$= \frac{10.243 \text{ U.S. motor vehicle deaths}}{100,000 \text{ people}}$$

Note that the denominator in the first factor is NOT in scientific notation form. (Why?) Do not change the 100,000 in the conversion factor to base 10, as the "100,000 people" is a required form in the problem response. (You are essentially creating a "100,000 people" unit, as needed in the response.)

Also, you should not report responses in scientific notation or with base 10 multipliers unless such forms are specified. While expressing the values using those forms makes for easier calculation, one purpose of dimensional analysis is to get numerical values in a form that is more easily understood, which for a general audience, would not be in product forms.

Sentence response:

In 2014, 32,675 people in the United States died in motor vehicles out of a population of about 319 million people; this is a rate of approximately 10.243 motor vehicle deaths per 100,000 people.

EXAMPLE 6A: Express 1 square foot in square inches.

$$1 \text{ square foot} \times \left(\frac{12 \text{ inches}}{1 \text{ foot}} \right)^2 = 144 \text{ square inches}$$

Remember that an exponent of 2 means multiply twice. So the squared conversion factor shown in the product expression above could also be expressed by multiplying the conversion factor twice instead of using the exponent.

EXAMPLE 6B: Express 1 square foot in square centimeters. *The metric prefix "centi" = 10^{-2} = one-hundredth.*

$$1 \text{ square foot} \times \left(\frac{12 \text{ inches}}{1 \text{ foot}} \right)^2 \times \left(\frac{2.54 \text{ centimeters}}{1 \text{ in}} \right)^2 = 929.0304 \text{ square centimeters}$$

Remember that an exponent of 2 means multiply twice. So the squared conversion factors shown in the product expression above could also be expressed by multiplying the conversion factors twice instead of using the exponents.

Note that these two examples to do not have sentence responses because they were not posed as contextual questions to be answered.

EXAMPLE 7: The pediatric dosage of acetaminophen is based on the child's weight. The conservative **dose is 10 milligrams per kilogram** at **four** equally spaced **doses each day.** One version comes in a suspension of **160 milligrams per 5 milliliters.** How many *milliliters* of this acetaminophen suspension would be required to give a **60-pound child** the appropriate dosage for **4 days**? Round to the nearest hundredth.

Note that "milli" shows up in two of the quantities. From the metric prefix table after Example 8, *milli = 10^{-3} = one-thousandth, so we have units of one-thousandth of a gram and one-thousandth of a liter. We also see "kilo" used again, this time for 1 kilogram = 1,000 gram.*

$$\frac{\frac{10 \text{ mg}}{1 \text{ kg}}}{1 \text{ dose}} \times \frac{4 \text{ doses}}{1 \text{ day}} \times \frac{5 \text{ ml}}{160 \text{ mg}} \times 60 \text{ lb} \times 4 \text{ days} \times \frac{0.4536 \text{ kg}}{1 \text{ lb}} = 136.08 \text{ mL}$$

Except for the last factor, all factors in this problem were given in the problem.

Sentence response:

Using conservative pediatric dosing standards for acetaminophen of 10 milligrams per kilogram given four times per day, over four days a 60-pound child would require a total of 136.08 milliliters of a 160 milligram per 5 milliliters suspension.

Before continuing your reading, complete the following.

YOUR TURN 3: The pediatric dosage of acetaminophen is based on the child's weight. The conservative dose is 10 milligrams per kilogram at four equally spaced doses each day. One version comes in a suspension of 160 milligrams per 5 milliliters. How many milliliters of this acetaminophen suspension would be required to give a 60-pound child the appropriate dosage for 4 days? Round the final answer to the nearest hundredth. This is the same problem as Example 7 but this time use the 8-decimal place exact equivalent of 1 pound = 0.45359237 kilogram.

In this kind of application, the 8-decimal place kilogram/pound exact conversion is not commonly used for manual calculations. The differences observed between the two calculations' results cannot be utilized in a reasonable fashion in most real-life situations. It would be nearly impossible for a parent to measure milliliters to the nearest ten-thousandth decimal place accuracy in a home environment. So, unlike the earlier watt/cost problems where the differences in using the 365 days – 1 year and the less accurate 52 weeks ≈ 1 year had a "real" measurable and practical impact, this problem illustrates a situation where a less precise conversion factor does not have a practical real-life impact.

EXAMPLE 8: According to June 16, 2015, article at Earthsky.org, earth has a new *quasi-satellite*. Not quite a moon, it is a small asteroid that has followed earth's orbit for at least 100 years and is expected to stay on that path for centuries. The article indicates that we have no reason to fear any sort of *close encounter* with our new companion, as its next closest visit in 2030 will be **14 million kilometers** from earth. What is that distance in meters? In miles?

$$14 \times 10^6 \text{ kilometers} \times \frac{10^3 \text{ meters}}{1 \text{ kilometer}} = 14 \times 10^6 \times 10^3 \text{ meters} = 14 \times 10^9 \text{ meters}$$

$$= 14,000,000,000 \text{ meters}$$

$$14 \times 10^6 \text{ kilometers} \times \frac{0.621 \text{ mile}}{1 \text{ kilometer}} = 14 \times 10^6 \times 0.621 \text{ miles} = 8,694,000 \text{ miles}$$

The earth's "new" celestial companion that experts have dubbed a quasi-satellite because it has been following earth's orbit for a hundred years, and will continue to do so for centuries, is a small asteroid whose next close visit will be at a distance of 14 billion meters or 14 million kilometers or 8,694,000 miles.

A real-life unit conversion crisis: Unit conversions and dimensional analysis are important in real life. Failure to pay attention to such details resulted in a very expensive error for NASA in 1999 when a mistake with units of measurement resulted in the loss of a $125 million Mars Climate Orbiter. Articles still abound about this mistake; here is a link to one: http://www.cnn.com/TECH/space/9909/30/mars.metric.02/.

Recognizing the metric prefixes and their corresponding powers of 10 can keep you from needing to memorize a lot unit equivalents. Here is a table from US Department of Commerce National Institute of Standards and Technology publication *NIST Handbook 44—2016, Appendix C*, http://www.nist.gov/pml/wmd/pubs/upload/appc-16-hb44-final.pdf.

yotta,	(Y),	meaning 10^{24}	deci,	(d),	meaning 10^{-1}
zetta,	(Z),	meaning 10^{21}	centi,	(c),	meaning 10^{-2}
exa,	(E),	meaning 10^{18}	milli,	(m),	meaning 10^{-3}
peta,	(P),	meaning 10^{15}	micro,	(µ),	meaning 10^{-6}
tera,	(T),	meaning 10^{12}	nano,	(n),	meaning 10^{-9}
giga,	(G),	meaning 10^{9}	pico,	(p),	meaning 10^{-12}
mega,	(M),	meaning 10^{6}	femto,	(f),	meaning 10^{-15}
kilo,	(k),	meaning 10^{3}	atto,	(a),	meaning 10^{-18}
hecto,	(h),	meaning 10^{2}	zepto,	(z),	meaning 10^{-21}
deka,	(da),	meaning 10^{1}	yocto,	(y),	meaning 10^{-24}

Thus, a kilometer is 1,000 meters and a millimeter is 0.001 meter.

YOUR TURN FINAL ANSWERS

1) See the indicated dictionary definitions.

2) $1,500 \text{ watts} \times \dfrac{3 \text{ hours}}{1 \text{ day}} \times \dfrac{5 \text{ days}}{1 \text{ week}} \times \dfrac{1}{4} \text{ year} \times \dfrac{8\cent}{\text{kilowatt} - \text{hour}} \times \dfrac{52 \text{ weeks}}{1 \text{ year}} \times \dfrac{1 \text{ kilowatt}}{1,000 \text{ watts}}$

$\times \dfrac{\$1}{100\cent} \approx \$23.40$

3) $\dfrac{\frac{10 \text{ mg}}{1 \text{ kg}}}{1 \text{ dose}} \times \dfrac{4 \text{ doses}}{1 \text{ day}} \times \dfrac{5 \text{ ml}}{160 \text{ mg}} \times 60 \text{ lb} \times 4 \text{ days} \times \dfrac{0.45359237 \text{ kg}}{1 \text{ lb}} = 136.077711 \text{ mL} \approx 136.08 \text{ mL}$

CHECK YOUR MASTERY

➢ **Chapter Terminology**: *If you do not know the meaning, record it here.*

Units of measurement

Unit (1)

Dimensional Analysis

Given Factor

Conversion Factor

Expression

Evaluated

Contextual

Self-Contained

➢ **Do you know:**

- *The conversion factors that your instructor expects you to memorize?*

- *The commonly used metric prefixes? (Everyone should know centi, milli, kilo)*

➢ **Can you:**

- Complete dimensional analysis problems involving units of time?

- Complete dimensional analysis problems related to costs of electricity?

- Complete dimensional analysis problems related to medication dosing?

- Complete dimensional analysis problems that express large quantities in rates per a specified quantity?

- Complete dimensional analysis problems involving common units of length or area?

- Complete dimensional analysis problems like those worked or assigned by your instructor?

- Write complete contextual and self-contained responses to each question that allows the reader to understand all problem details without access to the question or mathematical work?

EXERCISES

Use the provided unit equivalents in completing the problems in this exercise set. Remember that you must use standard abbreviations if you choose to abbreviate in the mathematical work. Abbreviations are not generally acceptable in sentences. (Money symbols are acceptable.)

Units of Time	
1 year (yr) = 365 days (d)	1 week = 7 days
1 day = 24 hours (h)	1 hour = 60 minutes (min)
1 minute = 60 seconds (s)	1 year ≈ 52 weeks (only used if indicated in problem because of increased errors in solutions!)

Units of Length	
1 mile (mi) = 5,280 feet (ft)	1 mile = 1,760 yards (yd)
1 foot = 12 inches	1 yard = 3 feet
1 inch (in) = 0.0254 meter (m)	1 inch = 2.54 centimeter (cm)
1 foot = 30.48 centimeter	1 foot = 0.3048 meter
1 yard = 0.9144 meter	1 kilometer (km) = 0.621 mile
1 kilometer = 1,000 meter	

Miscellaneous Units	
1 kilowatt (kW) = 1,000 watt (W)	1 pound (lb) ≈ 0.4536 kilogram (kg)
1 teaspoon (tsp) = 5 milliliter (mL)	$1.00 = 100¢

The numerical answers to the dimensional analysis work must be in mathematical form. But verbal form would be used in the sentences that answer the questions. For example:

$$\left(\text{mathematical form} : \frac{\$435.23}{\text{min}} \text{ vs. verbal form} : \$435.23 \text{ per minute} \right)$$

I) Use the dimensional analysis process discussed in this unit to express each of the following quantities in the units specified. Your response will be one numerical expression consisting of the original given factor(s) multiplied by the necessary unit conversion factors (equivalent to 1) leading to the final answer in the specified units.

1) Express one week in minutes.

2) Express one year in minutes.

3) Express 1 square yard in square inches.

4) Express 1 square yard in square centimeters.

5) A room's dimensions are 12 feet by 11 feet. Express the area of the room in square yards. Express the area of the room in square meters. Work these as two separate problems, starting with the original room dimensions for both calculations.

6) A room's dimensions are 12 feet by 11 feet. Express the area of the room in square inches. Express the area of the room in square centimeters. Work these as two separate problems, starting with the original room dimensions for both calculations.

II) Use the dimensional analysis process discussed in this unit to express each of the following quantities in the units specified. These problems have two parts.

- A single expression of multiple original given factors multiplied by the necessary unit conversion factor(s) leading to the answer in the specified units. Because of accuracy concerns, only use 52-week = 1 year conversions when specified.

- As each of these asks contextual questions, a self-contained contextual response must follow calculations. (It must be possible for reader to discern all details of the problem without reading the question or seeing the mathematical work.) Contextual questions, including those that require calculations to arrive at a numerical response numerical, need a contextual sentence that responds to the question.

7) According to a March 2015 USA Today article (http://www.usatoday.com), Starbucks had about $12.7 billion in US sales in 2014, making them the number two restaurant chain for sales. Based on this information, what were their sales in dollars (to the nearest cent) per minute?

8) According to that same March 2015 USA Today article (http://www.usatoday.com), Starbucks replaced Subway, the previous holder of the number two restaurant chain for sales. They indicated that Subway had about $11.9 billion in sales in 2014. Based on this information, what were the Subway sales in dollars (to the nearest cent) per hour?

9) According to the UN (http://aidsinfo.unaids.org/), about 1.4 million people died of HIV/AIDS worldwide in 2012. The estimated population of the world in 2012 was 7.1 billion people. What was the world's rate of death from HIV/AIDS in units of deaths (to nearest thousandth) per 100,000 people?

10) According to the UN (http://aidsinfo.unaids.org/) about 1.4 million people died of HIV/AIDS worldwide in 2012. The estimated population of the world in 2012 was 7.1 billion people. What was the world's rate of death from HIV/AIDS in units of deaths (to nearest thousandth) per 10,000 people?

11) You have 3,400-watt electric clothes dryer. On average, you estimate that you run the dryer 3 days per week for 4 hours per day throughout the year. How much money, in dollars to the nearest cent, does it cost you to run your dryer as indicated if the local electricity costs are $0.12 per kilowatt-hour?

12) You have an 1,800-watt hair dryer that you use for an average of 10 minutes per day. Your utility company charges $0.12 per kilowatt-hour of energy. How much does it cost you to run the hair dryer as indicated for a year? Report your results in dollars to the nearest cent.

13) Suppose you purchased a 1,200-watt electric ceramic heater to keep your room toasty at night when it is particularly cold. A one-week period was so cold, that you ran the heater for 18 hours per day. If the power company charges 10¢ per kilowatt-hour, what were your costs for running your heater as described in units of dollars the nearest cent (no other units can remain)?

14) A James Madison University (JMU) STAT faculty member's son-in-law recently ran the 2016 Boston Marathon in 3.0492 hours (3:02:57). The length of a marathon is 26.2 miles. On average, how fast did he run in feet per minute?

15) The complete statistical analyses of the 2016 Boston Marathon being unavailable, the 2015 (http://running.competitor.com/2015/) results were consulted and the average run time of male 30- to 34-year-old finishers was 3:23 or about 3.3833 hours. On average, how fast did competitors in this age group run in feet per minute?

16) The allergy medication diphenhydramine hydrochloride should be administered to children four equal size doses that sum to the daily maximum dosage of 5 mg/kg/day. The liquid suspension of the medication is 12.5 milligrams per 5 milliliters. How many milliliters per dose should a 70-pound child receive? In teaspoons? Work the parts as two separate problems. *Do not use your work from the first part of this problem to work the second.*

17) The pediatric dosage of acetaminophen is based on the child's weight. The maximum dose is 15 milligrams per kilogram per dose in four equally spaced doses each day. One version comes in a suspension of 160 milligrams per 5 milliliters. How many milliliters of this acetaminophen suspension would be required to give a 75-pound child the appropriate dosage for 5 days? What is the dosage size in teaspoons? (Use only the given factors from the description that are required to answer the second question; while the first question required all of the given factors, the second does not.) *Do not use your work from the first part of this problem to work the second.*

18) In 2009 about 1,300,000 people died of HIV/AIDS in sub-Saharan Africa. The estimated population of sub-Saharan Africa at that time was about 831,000,000. What was the rate of death from HIV/AIDS in units of deaths (to nearest hundredth) per 10,000 people?

19) In 2009 about 1,300,000 people died of HIV/AIDS in sub-Saharan Africa. The estimated population of sub-Saharan Africa at that time was about 831,000,000. What was the rate of death from HIV/AIDS in units of deaths (to hundredth) per 100,000 people?

20) A hot tub draws about 1,600 watts. Assume that the power company charges $0.11 per kilowatt-hour and that the spa runs the hot tub continuously for ¾ year. What is the cost (in dollars to the nearest cent) of running this appliance as indicated? Report your results in dollars to the nearest cent.

21) A hot tub draws about 1,800 watts. Assume that the power company charges $0.17 per kilowatt-hour and that the spa runs the hot tub continuously for 5/6 year. What is the cost of running this appliance as indicated? Report your results in dollars to the nearest cent.

22) Any individual person's actual heart rate at any point in time varies and depends on many things including age, health status, current stress or activity level, and general level of physical activity. For these calculations, assume that on average the heart rate is about 80 heartbeats per minute. According to the World Bank, http://data.worldbank.org/, the life expectancy of a person born in Sudan in 1996 is about 57 years. Provide the approximate number of heartbeats per lifetime for someone born in the Sudan in 1996.

23) Any individual person's actual heart rate at any point in time varies and depends on many things including age, health status, current stress or activity level, and general level of physical activity. For these calculations, assume that on average the heart rate is about 80 heartbeats per minute. According to the World Bank, http://data.worldbank.org/, the life expectancy of a person born in United States in 1996 is about 76 years. Provide the approximate number of heartbeats per lifetime for someone born in the United States in 1996.

24) The lamps in a room currently use three 60-watt incandescent light bulbs. The room is used every day, with all three bulbs in use for about 6 hours per day. The utility company charges 15¢ per kilowatt-hour of electricity. Use exact conversions.

a) What is the cost of electricity to use the lamps with the current bulbs for one year? Give your response in dollars to the nearest cent. Do not forget your sentence!

b) Now suppose that the lamps' bulbs were replaced with 15-watt compact fluorescent (CFL) bulbs that have about the same light output as the current incandescent bulbs. What is the cost of electricity to use the lamps with the CFL bulbs for one year? Give your response in dollars to the nearest cent. This time, however, start with electricity costs in the form $0.15 per kilowatt-hour. (Same cost but in a different form, which changes the numerical expression.) Do not forget your sentence!

c) For the third calculation, assume that the lamps' bulbs were replaced with 8-watt light emitting diode (LED) bulbs that have about the same light output as the current incandescent bulbs. What is the cost of electricity to use the lamps with the LED bulbs for one year? Use either form of the electricity cost that you wish. Give your response in dollars to the nearest cent. Do not forget your sentence!

d) Use the information from a to c to determine the one-year energy cost savings with CFL bulbs (as compared to the incandescent). Do the same for the LED bulbs. Show your work! Write a contextual sentence that explains the situation and compares the electricity cost savings. (Assume that your reader has not read any of the questions, answers, or calculations to this point.)

25) A recent Amazon.com check revealed that a pack of four 60-watt incandescent bulb cost $4.99. Those bulbs are rated to last 5,000 hours. A light producing equivalent 9-watt LED bulb, rated to last 30,000 hours, was sold in in packs of two for $10.49. An equivalent 13-watt CFL bulb, rated to last 10,000 hours, was sold in packs of eight for $13.28. Find the average cost per hour of a 60-watt incandescent bulb, a 9-watt LED bulb, and a 13-watt CFL bulb. Remember no side calculations! Write sentences expressing your argument for which bulb should be purchased.

CHAPTER 2
Quantifying and Communicating about Parts of a Whole, Change, Difference, and Ratio

CHAPTER OBJECTIVES

Upon completion of this chapter, the student should be able to

❑ Identify the numerical values of, as well as verbally describe, the part and whole quantities in percentage problems.

❑ Identify the numerical values of, as well as verbally describe, the reference and compared quantities in a quantitative comparison scenario.

❑ Illustrate the ability to work with quantitative comparisons (percentage, absolute and relative change, absolute and relative difference, or ratio) by writing the comparison expression and computing the numerical result (including units of measure, if appropriate).

❑ Write complete self-contained contextual interpretations for all comparison problem types, including all three interpretation forms for ratio.

The mathematical tools used in this chapter apply to most (if not all) fields of endeavor. Our media is certainly filled with quantitative information, some of which is effectively communicated and the rest which are completely misinterpreted and/or misstated. Even those majoring in or with degrees from quantitative fields, including Mathematics, often struggle with accurately communicating the meaning of quantitative information.

27

This chapter has two overarching goals. The first goal is to build mathematical competence with some of the most commonly used mathematical tools used across many fields: those that measure the proportion of some group with a certain characteristic; those that measure quantitative changes or comparisons between two values (absolute and relative changes/differences and ratios); and those that allow us to express, model, and calculate the impact of predictable changes over time or under varying conditions. The second goal, undoubtedly the more challenging task for nearly all students and for people in general, is to meaningfully interpret or communicate the results of these mathematical tools for a general audience. After writing your self-contained contextual interpretations, always ask yourself, *"Does this explanation/interpretation make sense if it is all the information available to the reader?"* before moving on to the next item.

2.1 PARTS OF A WHOLE

Fractions, decimals, and percentages have long been used to express "parts of a whole." Such usages are straightforward if we take care in identifying the "whole."

EXAMPLE 1: Consider the following data from the US Census Bureau publication "Monthly and Average Monthly Poverty Rates by Selected Demographic Characteristics: 2013."

Poverty by Selected Characteristics: 2013 *(all values in thousands)*		
Characteristic	**Total**	**Number in Poverty**
All people	310,275	53,040
Age		
Under 18 years	73,074	17,538
18–64 years	193,814	32,172
65 years and older	43,387	3,330
Sex		
Male	151,607	24,074
Female	158,668	28,966

Use the information in the table about US poverty to answer the following questions. For each problem, label the fraction/proportion (in context) that clearly identifies both the "whole" and the "part," then show the calculation (proportion and decimal), and then write a self-contained contextual response to the question.

a) Approximately what percentage of all people in the United States in 2013 lived in poverty?

First, label and calculate the fraction/proportion:

Proportion (or fraction) of all people in the United States in 2013 who lived in poverty

$$= \frac{53,040,000}{310,275,000} \approx 0.1709$$

Notice that the information prior to the *lived* in the question is the whole and what follows the *lived* is the part. Notice also that *lived* becomes *who lived* in the proportion statement.

Second, write the self-contained sentence, remembering to convert the decimal result to a percentage, as that is what the question asked.

According to the US Census Bureau publication "Monthly and Average Monthly Poverty Rates by Selected Demographic Characteristics: 2013," about 17.09% of the 310,275,000 people in the United States in 2013 lived in poverty.

b) Approximately what percentage of all people in the United States in 2013 were children (under 18 years)?

Fraction (or proportion) of all people in the United States in 2013 who were children

$$= \frac{73,074,000}{310,275,000} \approx 0.2355$$

According to the US Census Bureau, approximately 23.55% of the 310,275,000 people in the United States in 2013 were children.

c) Approximately what percentage of all people in the United States in 2013 were children who lived in poverty?

Proportion of all people in the United States in 2013 who were children living in poverty

$$= \frac{17,538,000}{310,275,000} \approx 0.0565$$

According to the US Census Bureau, approximately 5.49% of the 310,275,000 people in the United States in 2013 were children living in poverty.

d) Approximately what percentage of children in the United States in 2013 lived in poverty?

Fraction of all children in the United States in 2013 who lived in poverty

$$= \frac{17,538,000}{73,074,000} \approx 0.2400$$

According to the US Census Bureau, about 24% of the 73,074,000 children in the United States in 2013 lived in poverty.

Did you notice that each of the sentences included the denominator (whole) value to make the reported percentage value meaningful? Make sure that you always remember to include the denominator value after the "percent of" in your sentences.

Before continuing to the next section, complete the following:

YOUR TURN 1: Use the relevant information from the 2013 poverty table to answer the following questions. Show each calculation, including the proportion label like those shown in all parts of Example 1, and then write a self-contained contextual response to the question.

a) Approximately what percentage of all people in the United States in 2013 were between the ages of 18 and 64?

b) Approximately what percentage of all people in the United States in 2013 were both between the ages of 18 and 64 and living in poverty?

c) Approximately what percentage of people between the ages of 18 and 64 in the United States in 2013 lived in poverty?

2.2 CHANGES: COMPARISONS OF TWO QUANTITIES

Very little in life is constant or unchanging. It is often necessary, or at the very least useful, to quantify (or measure or express numerically) how a quantity changes over time or compares under varying conditions and, once that is accomplished, to then understand and effectively communicate about those results.

Most of the content of this section is presented via examples that first illustrate the mathematical comparison(s) to be made and then followed by exemplars for how those results should be *meaningfully communicated to others*.

An article accessed from Leesburg Today Online on August 15, 2013, titled "The Rise of College Tuition Slows" contained a great deal of quantitative information about yearly tuitions at several of Virginia's Universities (currently this media outlet is accessed via http://www.loudountimes.com). The article contained information for the anticipated fall 2013 tuitions and for tuitions from 2008 (five years earlier). The article's author provided information for tuitions at <u>two points in time</u> to allow the reader to quantify the changes in tuition rather than just taking the author's statement of change as fact.

Here is the key information from the article that will be used throughout the examples and Your Turn problems:

> **The article tells of one family's experiences in paying yearly tuitions at Virginia's universities. In fall 2013, their youngest daughter would attend University of Virginia, where the yearly tuition was an anticipated $12,458. Five years earlier (in fall 2008) the yearly tuition was about $9,300. The family's eldest daughter had actually started James Madison University (JMU) in fall 2008, when in-state tuition was about $6,666 per year. At the time of the article (fall 2013), JMU still had one of the lowest tuition rates among Virginia state universities at $9,176 a year.**

2.2.1 Change over Time: Comparing Values of a Quantity at Two Points in Time

There are two straightforward calculations to quantify changes over time. Order of the values is critical in both calculations as the *change* always uses the older value as the reference.

The first calculation, called **absolute change**, is very intuitive. It simply looks at the difference of the two quantitative values, as follows:

$$\textit{absolute change} = \textit{compared (or newer) quantity value}$$
$$- \textit{reference (or older) quantity value}$$

As is typical, the unit of measure associated with both values must be the same and the result will be in the same units as those used in the calculations **except** when the original quantities are in percentages. This is addressed in Section 2.2.3.

The second calculation, **relative change** (or percentage change when expressed in percentage form), is a quotient that looks at the absolute change in the values with respect to the older/reference value. The units of the numerator and denominator will always cancel and thus the results can only be expressed in otherwise unitless decimal or percentage forms.

$$\text{relative change} = \frac{\text{compared (newer) quantity value} - \text{reference (older) quantity value}}{\text{reference quantity}}$$

$$= \frac{\text{absolute change}}{\text{reference quantity}}$$

EXAMPLE 2: Using the information in bold right before Section 2.2.1 heading and the two change formulas to answer the following: How did the University of Virginia's yearly tuition change from the fall of 2008 to the fall of 2013? Do not forget the decimal place requirements: four decimal places in decimal form and two decimal places in percentage form except when specified otherwise. Be sure to include the appropriate units in both the calculations and responses. Give the relative change values in both decimal and percentage forms.

First complete the calculations. Always start with the label!

$$\text{absolute change} = \$12,458 - \$9,300 = \$3,158$$

$$\text{relative change} = \frac{\$12,458 - \$9,300}{\$9,300} \approx 0.3396; 33.96\%$$

Now move on to the self-contained contextual sentences.

Undoubtedly, writing the self-contained contextual interpretations based on the numerical results of the calculations is far more challenging to most students than the calculations. As you consider what to write, think of the audience who is going to listen to your presentation or read your report. In these real-life situations, the audience typically would not know the question(s) asked, the calculations that were completed nor would they have immediate access to the information upon which those calculations were based. So, your sentences must convey the context and key pieces of information **without using any mathematical terminology**. The terms absolute and relative change or difference and ratio will never be used in interpretive sentences. Remember your goal in communicating the information to the audience is to make the information as meaningful and easy to understand as possible and that means spelling it out very precisely! *Always remember to include the reference value in the sentence*.

The level of detail shown in the examples that follow is the level of detail expected in all interpretations.

Sentence response for absolute change:

The fall 2013 University of Virginia yearly tuition was $3,158 higher than its $9,300 yearly tuition in fall 2008.

Sentence response for relative change: (In sentences, always use the percentage form of the relative measure.)

> The University of Virginia's 2013 yearly tuition was about 33.96% higher than its $9,300 yearly tuition in 2008.

ANALYSIS of example responses: *Carefully study both sentences along with the bulleted information below. The sentences are likely longer and more detailed than what you would have initially written on your own. But this is not length for length's sake . . . look at what the sentences specifically convey to the reader:*

➤ *They convey the context by identifying the institution (University of Virginia), by defining the quantity being compared (yearly tuition), and by giving the exact years.*

➤ *By mentioning 2013 first, the statements make it clear that the 2013 value is being compared to the 2008 value. (You might think this is obvious, but many people think either value order is acceptable. Do not leave it open to interpretation; be explicit.)*

➤ *The use of "higher than," placed between the explicit descriptions of 2013 yearly tuition and 2008 yearly tuition, helps convey that the 2013 value would be derived by adding a change quantity to the 2008 value. (In the relative case, multiplication of [relative change × the 2008 value] would be required before that addition.)*

➤ *All of this is done without using any mathematical terminology that might confuse a general audience. Absolute and relative change or difference and ratio will never be used in interpretive sentences.*

EXAMPLE 3: Providing examples of what **should not be done** is risky. But there are some questionable comparison statements that show up so often (even in published works), that it seems a risk worth taking.

Common **unacceptable** comparison statements:

> *The University of Virginia's yearly tuition was $3,158 more in fall 2013 than it was in fall 2008.*
> *The University of Virginia's yearly tuition was 33.96% higher in fall 2013 than it was in fall 2008.*

From a communication point of view, what is wrong with the previous responses?

The primary problem is that the reader is left wondering, "$3,158 more than what?" and "33.96% higher than what?" because the reference value is not provided.

*Second set of common **unacceptable** comparison statements:*

> *From 2008 to 2013, the absolute change in University of Virginia's yearly tuition was $3,158.*
> *From 2008 to 2013, the relative change in University of Virginia's yearly tuition was 33.96%.*

From a communication point of view, what is wrong with these responses?

➢ First, the phrases absolute change and relative change are meaningless to most in a general audience and even those that recognize the labels will likely not recall their mathematical meaning.

➢ Without verbal clues that convey the exact order and descriptions of the quantities compared, most people in a general audience would have a difficult time understanding what the statements mean.

➢ And finally, there is no reference value provided, so the reader has no ability to discern the original values or put the information into perspective.

The take away of this discussion is that you need to use a few more words and give your readers the information they need to easily understand the comparison that was made. The goal is to communicate with your audience.

YOUR TURN 2: Use the information in bold right before Section 2.2.1 heading and the two change formulas to answer the following: How did James Madison University's yearly tuition change from the fall of 2008 to the fall of 2013? Find both the absolute and relative change results and then interpret both results using self-contained contextual sentences.

EXAMPLE 4: *Reference values are critical!* Imagine reading the following totally **hypothetical** headline/statement:

> "Over Just One Week of Classes, 100 Percent More Students Living in James Madison University Dormitories Develop Potentially Life-Threatening Disease."

If you did not know the headline was hypothetical, it would sound pretty frightening, especially if you happened to live in one of those dorms.

Upon reading the statement you would want to consider that MANY (perhaps nearly all) common illnesses are *potentially life threatening* for some high-risk individuals. And as a group, JMU students are likely not especially a high-risk group for succumbing to common diseases. This statement, like similar shocking statements that show up in at times in some media, was obviously one written for its "shock factor."

The purpose of looking at the headline is to begin to understand how useless (and potentially misleading) it is to express relative change without reporting the reference value information.

Ask yourself, does "100 percent more than" mean there **was** a huge increase in the number of ill students over a one-week period? The answer, you may be surprised to learn, is **No**!

While the increase in the number of ill students may have been large, without knowing the number of students that were ill at the beginning of the week, one really has no idea! Consider a few possibilities:

Number of Ill Students Beginning of Week 1	Number of Ill Students Beginning of Week 2	Relative Change Value in One Week (%)
1	2	100%
4	8	100%
50	100	100%

Note that each row of the table shows a pair of "*number of ill students*" values that result in a relative change in the number of ill students over one week of 100%. Are each of these "100% more than" situations equally alarming? As a dormitory student, would you be equally concerned for your health in hearing the following?

> *The number of students living with the disease in James Madison dormitories on Monday was 100% more than the one student living with the disease in the James Madison dorms on the previous Monday.*

> *The number of students living with the disease in James Madison dormitories on Monday was 100% more than the 50 students living with the disease in the James Madison dorms on the previous Monday.*

It is likely that most folks would tend to ignore the first statement, while the second might lead one to dig out the hand sanitizer and up the vitamin C intake.

Knowing the reference information, in addition to the absolute or relative measure, is key to putting relative measures into perspective as there are unlimited combinations of values that will lead to identical relative change/difference numerical results.

2.2.2 Differences: Comparing Values of a Quantity under Two Conditions (No Time Change)

The key to the examples in the previous section was that there was a change in time and that the reference value was the older value. But what if you are simply comparing the values of two related quantities, like the costs of the same item at two different stores? In such a situation, there is no "time" element to determine the reference quantity. In such situations, **absolute differences** and **relative differences** are used. As you look at these formulas, they should look familiar, as they are essentially the same as those for absolute change and relative change, without the "time":

$$absolute\ difference = compared\ quantity\ value - reference\ quantity\ value$$

$$relative\ difference = \frac{compared\ quantity\ value - reference\ quantity\ value}{reference\ quantity\ value}$$

As with the change formulas, the values must be placed into the difference formulas in the appropriate order; otherwise the absolute results will have incorrect signs and the relative results will have both incorrect values and incorrect signs. Since we do not have time frames to indicate order, the primary difficulty that some experience is determining which value is the reference quantity. That information is always provided in the way the question is asked, as illustrated in the next example.

Once again, here is the key information from the article that is being used:

The article tells of one family's experiences in paying yearly tuitions at Virginia's universities. In fall 2013, their youngest daughter would attend University of Virginia, where the yearly tuition was an anticipated $12,458. Five years earlier (in fall 2008) the yearly tuition was about $9,300. The family's eldest daughter began to attend James Madison University in fall 2008, when in-state tuition was about $6,666 per year. At the time of the article (fall 2013), JMU still had one of the lowest tuition rates among Virginia state universities at $9,176 a year.

EXAMPLE 5: Use the bolded information on the previous page and the two difference formulas to answer the following: How did the yearly tuition at University of Virginia in fall 2013 compare to James Madison University's yearly tuition in fall 2013?

*Notice that in the question we are told UVA tuition is compared **to** the JMU tuition, so JMU's yearly tuition value is the reference. With the reference value identified, the work is essentially the same as it was with the change problems. Start with the calculations, then write appropriate self-contained contextual sentences.*

$$absolute\ difference = \$12,458 - \$9,176 = \$3,282$$

$$relative\ difference = \frac{\$12,458 - \$9,176}{\$9,176} \approx 0.3577\ or\ 35.77\%$$

Sentence response for absolute difference:

The yearly tuition at the University of Virginia in the fall 2013 tuition was $3,282 higher than James Madison University's $9,176 fall 2013 yearly tuition.

Sentence response for relative difference:

University of Virginia's yearly tuition in the fall 2013 tuition was about 35.77% higher than James Madison University's $9,176 fall 2013 yearly tuition.

If you are unsure about the strengths and weaknesses of different potential sentences, revisit the ANALYSIS discussions that followed **Example 2** and the unacceptable options presented in **Example 3** in the previous section!

YOUR TURN 3A: How did the fall 2013 JMU yearly tuition compare to UVA's yearly tuition that year? Find both the absolute and relative differences and then interpret using the appropriate self-contained sentences.

YOUR TURN 3B: Did you notice that the signs in the Your Turn 3a problems were opposite of those from Example 4? In those same problems, how do the percentage values of the relative differences compare? While the absolute difference values are the same except for the sign, that is not the case for the relative differences. Why?

2.2.3 Percentage (%) versus Percentage Point

Before moving on to other comparison methods, it is important to mention the slight challenge introduced when the change or difference quantities are themselves expressed in percentages.

EXAMPLE 6: You recently received a notice that in two months the interest rate on your credit card will go from its current rate of 12% to 14%. How is the interest rate on your credit card about to change?

$$absolute\ change = 14\% - 12\% = 2\ percentage\ points$$

$$relative\ change = \frac{14\% - 12\%}{12\%} \approx 0.1667\ or\ 16.67\%$$

Sentence response for absolute change:

Your recent credit card notification indicated that in two months your credit card interest rate will be 2 percentage points higher than the 12% current rate.

Sentence response for relative change:

Your recent credit card notification indicated that in two months your credit card interest rate will be about 16.67% higher than the 12% current rate.

Compare the two sentence responses. Consider what you would see if you replaced "percentage points" with "%" in the first sentence.

Suppose that your absolute change sentence said (**Remember this is INCORRECT**):

Your recent credit card notification indicated that in two months your credit card interest rate will be 2% higher than the 12% current rate.

INCORRECT sentence response for relative change:

> Your recent credit card notification indicated that in two months your credit card interest rate will be about 16.67% higher than the 12% current rate.

Obviously 2% and 16.67% are not expressing the same comparisons. But anyone seeing two otherwise identical statements would have no choice but to think there was some sort of error! The error is in the units used in the absolute statement!

Even worse, if only the absolute change was presented using "%," the reader would likely think it a relative change statement . . . one that grossly understates the actual relative change. The ONLY verbal clue that a reader has in the first statement is about an absolute change is the use of **percentage points**. If you are looking at the calculations themselves, the two quantitative results are different and mean two very different things.

*Again, remember that **your audience would not see the calculations**,* as is the case in almost every use of quantitative information that we communicate to others or have communicated to us! Without the distinction of "percentage points," a reader is left to wonder whether the difference expressed is absolute or relative or if some sort of error has been made. You must use percentage points as the units for absolute change/difference whenever the original quantities are in percentages.

2.2.4 Ratios

The most commonly used mathematical tools for comparing the values of two related quantities are ratios; in fact, relative changes and relative differences are themselves ratios. Most of us tend to think of ratios only in their fractional forms. But a lot of the quantitative information reported in the media is the result of a ratio calculation and we simply do not recognize them as expressing "ratios" when conveyed in sentence form. As with all other mathematical comparisons in this chapter, the order that values are inserted into the numerical expression and in the self-contained contextual interpretations is critical. In ratio comparisons, the numerator value is the compared quantity and the denominator value is the reference quantity. Like the earlier relative comparisons, the original units of measurement will always cancel but should be included in the calculation initially!

EXAMPLE 7: Given the ratio, $\dfrac{quantity\ a\ value}{quantity\ b\ value} = 3$, here are the three generic verbal forms that express this comparison.

Your statements must always reflect the ratio comparison order.

1) As a "times" or multiplier statement:

Quantity a's value is three times quantity b's value or

Quantity a's value is triple quantity b's value. ("triple" is equivalent to "three times.")

A ratio IS a multiplier, so this form expresses the ratio in its true form. Ratios are always in decimal form. (So no percentage values in the calculation results!) The other two verbal forms, though they express the same comparison, are not true ratio statements

2) As a "percent of" statement:

Quantity a's value is 300 percent of quantity b's value.

(300% is the percentage form of the decimal value of 3, recall "of" implies multiplication.)

3) As a "percent more/less than" statement:

Quantity a's value is 200 percent more than quantity b's value.

Note the relationship between forms 2 and 3. The value for the third form is always found by subtracting 100% from the value in form 2. Here, the calculation is *300% − 100% = 200%*. This third form essentially states: *200% of quantity b's value + 100% of quantity b's value = 300% of quantity b's value*, which is form 2.

This last interpretive sentence form (as well as the numerical value) is identical to that of the relative change or difference comparison using the same values and comparison order.

The decision between more than and less than is "not" the writer's choice. It depends on whether the difference value is positive or negative. If the difference is positive, there will be a percent more than statement. If the difference is negative, there will be a percent less than statement. DO NOT FLIP THE ORDER OF THE QUANTITIES IN YOUR SENTENCES; DOING SO MAKES THEM INCORRECT! Your statements must always reflect the comparison order of the ratio.

EXAMPLE 8: The size of the city's current population is double its original population size of 400 people. (The term "double" is equivalent to "two times.")

➤ What is the ratio calculation associated with this statement?

$$Ratio = \frac{current\ population\ size}{original\ population\ size} = \frac{800}{400} = 2.$$

➤ State the two percentage form interpretations for the provided *times* statement.

As a "percent of" statement:

> The city's current population size is 200 percent of its original population size of 400 people.

As a "percent more/less than" statement:

> The city's current population size is 100 percent more than its original population size of 400 people.

EXAMPLE 9: Once again revisit the University of Virginia's yearly tuition change from fall 2008 to fall 2013. Recall that their fall 2013 yearly tuition was $12,458 and in fall 2008 it was $9,300. Find the ratio of the new tuition to the old tuition. Then, convey that relationship in the three ways illustrated.

$$\text{Ratio:} \quad \frac{new\ UVA\ tuition}{old\ UVA\ tuition} = \frac{\$12,458}{\$9,300} \approx 1.3396$$

➤ As a multiplier (times):
The fall 2013 University of Virginia yearly tuition was about 1.3396 times its $9,300 fall 2008 yearly tuition.

➤ As a "percentage of":
The fall 2013 University of Virginia yearly tuition was about 133.96% of its $9,300 yearly tuition in fall 2008.

➤ As a "percentage more/less than":
The fall 2013 University of Virginia yearly tuition was about 33.96% higher than its $9,300 fall 2008 yearly tuition.

Does the last sentence look familiar? It is simply a minor variation of the relative change sentence in Example 2 of this chapter.

A caution on communication. You should NEVER use statements like "ten times more than" or "three times less than." These phrases, while grammatically acceptable, are mathematically questionable as their exact mathematical meanings are ambiguous. The only way for a reader to be certain of the exact meaning in any specific situation is to reconstruct the comparison calculations, IF all information required for such calculations happens to be available, which would rarely be the case. Such effort on the part of the reader should not be necessary to understand statements that supposedly interpret the results of a mathematical calculation for them!

"Times" implies multiplication, "more than" implies addition and "less than" implies subtraction but what operation is "times more than"? If you perform a search on "times more than" you will find lots of hits from both grammatical and mathematical experts, all of whom are still debating this issue! You will also find news articles that use this or similar language and leave some scratching their heads in trying to figure out the numerical meaning! You will see and hear such statements in the media. Such statements are confusing and their mathematical meaning uncertain, so use of "times more than or times less than" is unacceptable. We want to make understanding as easy as possible for our readers. **For clear communication, use "times" alone in comparison statements when reporting ratio results as a multiplier for the reference value.**

YOUR TURN 4: Use a ratio to compare James Madison University's yearly tuition in fall 2013 to its yearly tuition in fall 2008. Then, convey that relationship in the three ways illustrated in Example 9.

YOUR TURN FINAL ANSWERS

Section 2.1

1) a) *Proportion of all people in the United States in 2013 who were between the ages of* 18 *and* 64 $= \dfrac{193,814,000}{310,275,000} \approx 0.6247$. In 2013, about 62.47% of the 310,275,000 people in the United States were between the ages of 18 and 64.

   b) *Proportion of all people in the United States in 2013 who were both between the ages of* 18 *and* 64 *and living in poverty* $= \dfrac{32,172,000}{310,275,000} \approx 0.1037$. In 2013, 10.37% of the 310,275,000 people in the United States were both between the ages of 18 and 64 and living in poverty.

   c) *Proportion of all people between the ages of* 18 *and* 64 *in the United States in 2013 who lived in poverty* $= \dfrac{32,172,000}{193,814,000} \approx 0.1660$. In 2013, 16.6% of the 193,814,000 18- to 64-year-old people in the United States lived in poverty.

Section 2.2

2) *absolute change* $= \$9,176 - \$6,666 = \$2,510$ James Madison University's yearly tuition in the fall 2013 was $2,510 higher than its approximate $6,666 yearly tuition in fall 2008.
   relative change $= \dfrac{\$9,176 - \$6,666}{\$6,666} \approx 0.3765; 37.65\%$; The fall 2013 yearly tuition at James Madison University was about 37.65% above its approximate $6,666 yearly tuition in fall 2008.

3) a) *absolute difference* $= \$9,176 - \$12,458 = -\$3,282$; James Madison University's yearly tuition in the fall 2013 was $3,282 lower than the University of Virginia's $12,458 yearly tuition in fall 2013.
   relative difference $= \dfrac{\$9,176 - \$12,458}{\$12,458} \approx -0.2634; -26.34\%$; James Madison University's yearly tuition in the fall 2013 was about 26.34% lower than the University of Virginia's $12,458 yearly tuition in fall 2013.

   b) *This is a question to simply get you to stop and think for a moment, so that you don't later make an error in haste leading you to think, "oh, the signs just switch."*
   The absolute difference values of Example 4 and Your Turn 2a differ only in the sign. The same values are used but their order in the formula is reversed, so the signs are opposite. With the relative difference calculations, the numerator values are reversed, AND the denominator value is different. The change in reference value in the numerator AND denominator leads to a relative difference that differs both in sign AND value.

YOUR TURN FINAL ANSWERS

4) ***Ratio***: $\dfrac{\$9,176}{\$6,666} \approx 1.3765$

- As a multiplier (times): James Madison University's fall 2013 yearly tuition was about 1.3765 times its $6,666 fall 2008 yearly tuition.

- As a "percentage of": The fall 2013 James Madison University yearly tuition was about 137.65% of its $6,666 fall 2008 yearly tuition.

- As a "percentage more/less than": The fall 2013 James Madison University yearly tuition was about 37.65% higher than its $6,666 fall 2008 yearly tuition.

CHECK YOUR MASTERY

➤ **Chapter Terminology**: *If you do not know the meaning, record it here.*

Whole

Part

Absolute Change

Relative Change

Absolute Difference

Relative Difference

Reference Quantity

Compared Quantity

Percentage Points

Ratio

➤ **Do you know:**

- The absolute and relative change/difference formulas?

- When to use percentage points?

- The required language for interpretations: absolute and relative change/difference and three forms for ratio?

➤ **Can you:**

- Write proportion labels that clearly identify/describe the whole and the part?

- Write complete self-contained contextual responses to the percentage questions?

- Determine reference and compared quantities for absolute and relative change/difference problems?

- Write complete self-contained contextual interpretations for absolute and relative change/difference problems?

- Determine reference and compared quantities for ratio problems?

- Write the three forms of complete self-contained contextual interpretations for ratio problems?

EXERCISES

Do not forget to report decimal answers to the nearest ten-thousandths and percentages to nearest hundredths.

I) The table below is the same table used in the example and Your Turn problems in the opening section of this chapter.

Consider the following data from the 2017 US Census Bureau publication "Monthly and Average Monthly Poverty Rates by Selected Demographic Characteristics: 2013."

Poverty by Selected Characteristics: 2013		
(all values in thousands)		
Characteristic	**Total**	**Number in poverty**
All people	310,275	53,040
Age		
Under 18 years	73,074	17,538
18–64 years	193,814	32,172
65 years & older	43,387	3,330
Sex		
Male	151,607	24,074
Female	158,668	28,966

Use the information from the table on 2013 US poverty to answer the following questions. Label the needed proportion (remember full context descriptions of the "whole" and "part"), show each calculation with its decimal answer, including the proportion label like those shown in all parts of Example 1, and then write the self-contained contextual response to the question.

1) Approximately what percentage of all people living in the United States in 2013 were 65 years or older?

2) Approximately what percentage of all people living in the United States in 2013 were both 65 years or older and lived in poverty?

3) Approximately what percentage of people aged 65 years or older living in the United States in 2013 lived in poverty?

4) Approximately what percentage of all people living in the United States in 2013 were male?

5) Approximately what percentage of all people living in the United States in 2013 were female?

6) Approximately what percentage of all males living in the United States in 2013 lived in poverty?

7) Approximately what percentage of all females in the United States in 2013 lived in poverty?

8) Approximately what percentage of all people were females living in poverty?

II) Each of the following problems presents a scenario that can be summarized either by measures of absolute and relative change OR absolute and relative difference. For each problem

- Identify as change or difference with appropriate labeling of each calculation.

- Show the calculation setups (the numerical expression) and numerical results. These results, including percentages, may be negative. Do not forget to attach units where appropriate including % and percentage points. Give the relative measure in both decimal and percentage forms.

- Write complete self-contained contextual interpretations of both measures.

9) A news report says "the American Booksellers Association, which represents independent booksellers, currently represents 1,500 businesses. Twenty years ago, the American Booksellers Association represented 4,700 businesses." Find and discuss the relevant comparative absolute and relative measures.

10) In 1990, the number of people living with HIV in the world was about 8 million. By the end of 2011 the worldwide number of people living with HIV was about 34 million. Find and discuss the relevant comparative absolute and relative measures.

11) In 2014, the SAT participation rate among college-bound seniors in the 50 states and the District of Columbia varied from a low of 2.3% to a high of 100%. Compare the highest SAT participation rate to the lowest SAT participation rate.

12) In 2014, the SAT participation rate among college-bound seniors in the 50 states and the District of Columbia varied from a low of 2.3% to a high of 100%. Compare the lowest SAT participation rate to the highest SAT participation rate.

13) The percentage of Republicans in the House of Representatives was 40.9% in 2010 and 55.6% in 2012. Find and discuss the relevant comparative absolute and relative measures.

14) In 1990, the worldwide number of deaths of children under age 5 was about 12.7 million. In 2015, the number of deaths of children under age 5 was expected to be about 5.9 million. Find and discuss the relevant comparative absolute and relative measures.

III) Each of the following problems asks for a ratio comparison. For each problem:

- Show the calculation setup (the numerical expression) and numerical results.

- Using only the results of this one calculation, write the three complete, self-contained contextual interpretations that convey the ratio comparison results (*times, percent of, and percent less than/more than*). Order is critical in calculations and in the sentences.

15) In 1990, the number of people living with HIV in the world was about 8 million. By the end of 2011 the worldwide number of people living with HIV was about 34 million. What was the ratio of the number of people living with HIV in the world in 2011 to the number of people living with HIV in the world in 1990?

16) In 1990, the number of people living with HIV in the world was about 8 million. By the end of 2011 the worldwide number of people living with HIV was about 34 million. What was the ratio of the number of people living with HIV in the world in 1990 to the number of people living with HIV in the world in 2011?

17) In 1990, the worldwide number of deaths of children under age 5 was about 12.7 million. In 2015, the number of deaths of children under age 5 is expected to be about 5.9 million. What is the ratio of the worldwide number of deaths of children under age 5 in 1990 to the number of deaths of children under age 5 in the world in 2015?

18) In 1990, the worldwide number of deaths of children under age 5 was about 12.7 million. In 2015 the number of deaths of children under age 5 is expected to be about 5.9 million. What is the ratio of the worldwide number of deaths of children under age 5 in 2015 to the number of deaths of children under age 5 in the world in 1990?

19) According to the IUCN website www.iucn.org/what/biodiversity/, the International Union for Conservation of Nature has been assessing the status of species and subspecies for 50 years in hopes of maintaining the biodiversity of our planet. Each year, they compile a "red list" of threatened plants and animals. In January 2016, there were 23,250 species on the list. Ten years earlier, 2006, there were 16,119 species on the list. What is the ratio of the number of threatened plants and animals in 2016 to the number of threatened plants and animals in 2006?

20) According to the IUCN website www.iucn.org/what/biodiversity/, the International Union for Conservation of Nature has been assessing the status of species and subspecies for 50 years in hopes of maintaining the biodiversity of our planet. Each year they compile a "red list" of threatened plants and animals. In January 2016, there were 23,250 species on the list. Ten years earlier, in 2006, there were 16,119 species on the list. What is the ratio of the number of threatened plants and animals in 2006 to the number of threatened plants and animals in 2016?

CHAPTER 3
Linear and Exponential Expressions and Functions

CHAPTER OBJECTIVES

Upon completion of this chapter, the student should be able to

❑ Write and evaluate numerical and algebraic expressions for linear and exponential growth/decay.

❑ Label and describe completely independent and dependent variables, then write the linear or exponential function that conveys the relationship between the variables.

❑ Write complete self-contained contextual interpretations of the slope and y intercept in the forms specified.

❑ Identify and describe the individuals, explanatory and response variables for a described bivariate association.

❑ Demonstrate the ability to complete the self-contained contextual written analysis for a described bivariate association illustrated with a scatterplot.

Linear and exponential *expressions* are used to express and calculate the numerical results for many real-world situations involving quantities that change predictably over units of time or conditions. Linear and exponential *functions* are used to model many real-world relationships between variables. It is important to understand and effectively communicate about those models and associated graphs.

3.1 LINEAR AND EXPONENTIAL EXPRESSIONS

An *expression* is a mathematical phrase composed of numbers, variables, and/or mathematical operators that represents a numerical quantity. Expressions, unlike equations, are one-sided. There are two types of expressions:

➤ **Numerical expressions** are made up of one or more terms consisting entirely of numbers and mathematical operators; they can be simplified using the order of operations to arrive at the specific numerical value. Examples of numerical expressions: **5 + 2(3)**, **3²**, four times three squared.
➤ **Algebraic expressions** are made up of terms consisting of numbers, variables, and mathematical operators; they can sometimes be *simplified* using order of operations and combining like terms to arrive at the simplified form. They can be *evaluated* by substituting numerical values for the variables. Examples of algebraic expressions: four more than a number (4 + *x*), a number squared minus twice the number (**$x^2 - 2x$**), **4*x* + 2 + 6*x* − 5**

When a quantity changes by the same absolute amount in each unit of time it is said to show **linear growth/decay**. Growth involves positive fixed-change values and decay involves negative fixed-change values. Linear growth/decay expressions are represented in the following form:

Initial value + fixed absolute amount (number of time units)

The same basic setup expression can be used when conditions like the number of items are changing, rather than time. Simply replace "number of time units" with "number of (state the item that is changing)."

EXAMPLE 1a: Joyce *currently* has $350 in her bank account and has committed to adding $50 to that account each month. Without considering interest, how much money will be in her account at the end of 10 months? After 15 months? Write the appropriate numerical expression, then use order of operations to arrive at its numerical value.

$$\$350 + \frac{\$50}{\text{month}} \left(10 \text{ months}\right) = \$850$$

$$\$350 + \frac{\$50}{\text{month}} \left(15 \text{ months}\right) = \$1100$$

Note where each piece of information presented in the problem description is used in the expressions. Note that the expressions themselves are one sided, as stated earlier. Only when the expression is completely simplified to arrive at a single numerical value will the equal sign and numerical result be included.

EXAMPLE 1b: Joyce currently has $350 in her bank account and has committed to adding $50 to that account each month. Without considering interest, how much money will be in her account at the end of t months? Write the appropriate algebraic expression in terms of t.

$$\$350 + \frac{\$50}{month}\left(t \text{ months}\right)$$

Exponential growth/decay occurs when a quantity is changing by the same fixed relative amount in each unit of time. Growth involves positive change values and decay involves negative change values. Exponential growth/decay expressions are generally represented in the following form:

Initial value (1 + relative change amount in decimal form)$^{\text{number of time units}}$

EXAMPLE 2a: Joyce currently has $350 in her bank account and has committed to increasing the monetary value of the account by 11% each month. Without considering interest, how much money will be in her account at the end of 10 months? After 15 months? Write the appropriate numerical expression and record its value.

$$\$350 \, (1 + 0.11)^{10 \text{ months}} \approx \$993.80$$

$$\$350 \, (1 + 0.11)^{15 \text{ months}} \approx \$1674.61$$

EXAMPLE 2b: Joyce currently has $350 in her bank account and has committed to increasing the monetary value of the account by 11% each month. Without considering interest, how much money will be in her account at the end of t months? Write the appropriate algebraic expression.

$$\$350 \, (1 + 0.11)^{t \text{ months}}$$

YOUR TURN 1: According to information available from James Madison University's website, the in-state per semester tuition costs at James Madison University (JMU) have increased at the beginning of each academic year (fall) over the past 15 years. In 2010/2011, the tuition at JMU was $3,930 per semester and in 2011/2012 the tuition at JMU was $4,224 per semester. Note that these are semester tuition comparisons not yearly comparisons.

a) What was the absolute change in the in-state tuition per semester from fall 2010 to fall 2011?

Show the calculation and write a complete contextual self-contained sentence communicating this information to someone that has no knowledge of the information presented here. (Use the techniques from Chapter 2 in parts a) and b).)

b) If the ABSOLUTE change in per semester tuition costs at JMU remained constant since fall 2011, what would the expected per semester tuition costs be in fall 2016 (five years)? Write the numerical expression and provide the numerical answer.

c) Write the algebraic expression that could be used to find the expected tuition in any year under this same rate of growth. *Year 2011 would be year 0, t = time in years after 2011*

d) What was the relative change in the in-state tuition per semester from fall 2010 to fall 2011?

Show the calculation and write a complete contextual self-contained sentence communicating this information to someone that has no knowledge of the information presented here. (Use the techniques from Chapter 2.)

e) If the tuition costs at JMU had increased by the same relative amount (it has not) since fall 2011, what would the expected tuition costs be in fall 2016 (five years)? Write the numerical expression and provide the numerical answer.

f) Write the algebraic expression that could be used to find the expected tuition in any year under this same rate of growth. *Year 2011 would be year 0, t = time in years after 2011*

EXAMPLE 3: Your neighbor is going on a trip and asks you to look after her kitties. The "job" entails going to the house for an hour each day to visit with and feed the two cats and look after their "box." She will be gone for 14 days and offers you one of two options. She will either pay you $10 for each day starting with the first full day that she is gone (day 1) OR she will pay you $0.01 on the day that she leaves (day 0), double the previous days payment amount of $0.01 on day 1 (thus paying $0.02 for day 1) and continue to double the previous day's payment amount on each day that she is away. Which payment method should you take?

a) To answer this question, let t be the number of days worked and write the two relevant algebraic expressions that represent the total payment up to and including that day.

Income under the first payment option can be expressed algebraically by:

$$\$0 + \frac{\$10}{day}\left(t \text{ days}\right), \text{ which simplifies to } \frac{\$10}{day}\left(t \text{ days}\right)$$

Income under the second payment option can be expressed algebraically by:

$$\$0.01 \times 2^{t \text{ days}}$$

Are you asking yourself, where the heck did this come from?

Think back to the ratio discussion in the previous chapter. Recall that "double" means "2 times." Under this payment scheme, the income will "double" each day, meaning the previous day's income value will be multiplied by two on each consecutive day worked. So, this expression is a variation on the earlier exponential growth expression that takes each day's doubling into account. Keep this in mind for the next Your Turn!

b) Evaluate the two expressions for 14 completed days of work to determine which method will lead to your greater income.

Let $t = 14$ and substitute the 14 as a replacement for t in the expression:

Income under the first payment option: $\frac{\$10}{day}\left(14 \text{ days}\right) = \$140$

Income under the second payment option: $\$0.01 \times 2^{14 \text{ days}} = \$163.84$

c) Make your decision and justify.

Given that the "kitty sitting" income under the exponential payment scheme starting at $0.01 results in a $23.84 higher income after 14 days than the $10 a day scheme, it only makes sense to ask for the exponential scheme for payment.

This is a good time to take a look at graphs exhibiting linear and exponential growth.

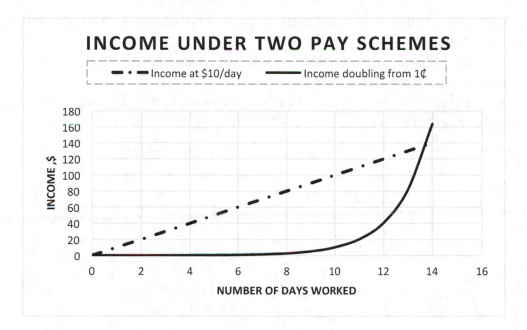

Substituting the values for the *number of days worked* into the two algebraic expressions results in data to produce a graph similar to the one above.

The dashed line shows the linear relationship, the solid line shows the exponential relationship.

Linear and exponential growth patterns always show shapes like those seen here.

Exponential growth may be less familiar to you than linear growth, so the big takeaway is that exponential growth may start out very slowly but will ultimately lead to ever increasing and steeper growth overall.

Introductions to growth and decay models emphasize changes to quantities in response to changes over time, but as we see in this next Your Turn, the same basic forms also apply to nontime–related changes as well.

YOUR TURN 2: An online search for **exponential growth stories, folktales** or **legends** will result in several different versions of a story about a great king or some other larger than life leader, a chessboard, and grains of rice or wheat. These stories have long existed and there are even children's books written that tell the basic story. In the various versions, this great leader is introduced to the game of chess by its creator. The leader is so overjoyed by the experience that he begs the creator to allow him (the leader) to give him (the creator) some great gift. The king is very surprised when the gift requested is for grain (either rice or wheat) distributed as follows: one grain is placed on square 1, two grains on square 2, four grains on square 3, eight grains on square 4, 16 grains on square 5, and so on, all the way up to square 64.

a) Fill in the table using the described pattern.

    I) Start by filling in the second row of the provided grid. Consider how the number of grains on each square is related.

    II) Write each value for the number of grains as a power of two. Consider how the power relates to the square ID number.

    III) Letting n represent the number of the square, what is the algebraic expression for the number of grains on square n? Add this to the grid.

Square ID Number	1	2	3	4	5	. . .n
Number of grains on square	1					
Number of grains on square as power of 2	2^0					
Total number of grains on board as of square id number						

b) Now consider how many grains are on the entire board up to and including any given numbered square. As of only square 1, there is one grain in total; as of square 2, there are three grains in total; as of square 3 there are seven grains.

    I) As of square 4, there are _____ grains in total on the board.

    II) As of square 5, there are _____ grains in total on the board.

    III) What is this pattern, with respect to the number of the square, n? In other words, what algebraic expression represents the total number of grains on the board up to and including square n? Add each of the values from b) to the grid.

c) Using your two algebraic expressions, how many grains are on square 20 of the chess board? How many grains are on the board up to and including square 20? Show the work!

d) According to the U.S. Rice Producers Association (http://www.usriceproducers.com), there are about 29,000 grains of long grain white rice in 1 pound. If this is the type of rice being placed on the chess board, what is the approximate weight (in pounds) of the rice on the board up to and including square 20? (This is a dimensional analysis problem; remember all work, including the units of measure!)

3.2 MODELLING LIFE WITH LINEAR AND EXPONENTIAL FUNCTIONS

In this chapter, we have written linear and exponential numerical expressions that express the value of described growth/decay quantities at a specified point in time or specific conditions. In each case, the problem provided the exact numbers to use, including starting value, rate of change, and the number of time frames, along with information that indicated growth or decay. By simplifying the expressions, we were able to find the value of tuition in a specific year, income after a specified number of days, and so on. In some cases, we went a step further and wrote algebraic expressions that expressed the values of the described quantities for unspecified time t.

The next logical step is to write functions to model the relationships between the two variables in these sorts of relationships; writing such functions was a key topic in the algebra classes of your past. We will not rehash all the related mathematical concepts from algebra classes, like the formal definitions of functions that start with discussions of ordered pairs and relations and quickly move on to domains, ranges, graphs, vertical line tests, and so forth. We will not even find slopes and point-slope forms of lines. Instead, we will look at functions as models for real-world relationships between related but varying quantities. Our focus will be on connections between verbal descriptions, mathematically expressed functions, and related interpretations.

With this more application and interpretation focus, our "definition" of function will be less formal than mathematical definitions you saw in your earlier coursework, but our definition hearkens back to early historical notions of what a "function" was.

➢ We approach functions as mathematical representations of real-world relationships between related quantities where the value of one quantity (dependent variable) depends on and varies predictably with the value of another quantity (independent variable). *"Depends on" does not necessarily imply causes. More on this later.*

- The functions we will use are described by algebraic expressions of known constant values, mathematical operators, and single independent variables.
- By inputting different values of the independent variable into these functions we will be able to determine (or at least estimate) the associated value of the dependent variable.
- We will focus on two types of functions, linear and exponential, and will limit our scenarios to those that involve one dependent variable and one independent variable.
- Although many of these scenarios build from earlier problems involving time frames as independent variables, some will involve other scenarios where the independent variable is not a time frame.

Definition: A function is a mathematical rule, (the algebraic expression), that describes mathematically how the value of the dependent variable (often y) will respond when a specified value of the independent variable (often x or t) is input into the expression. Any appropriate value can replace the variable in the expression. When we evaluate the function for an input value, it will result in exactly one corresponding output value.

Input a value of $x \rightarrow f(x) \rightarrow$ Output a value of y

---

EXAMPLE 4: One final consideration before we begin looking at applications: previously you may have heard the terms *equation* and *function* used interchangeably but we can easily observe through a few examples that though certainly related they really are not exactly the same.

- An equation is solved, and its solution(s) found, by equating two expressions and solving for the variable. (Appendix I has examples and problems for solving equations). For example:

$$3x + 1 = 5 \qquad\qquad x^2 - 4 = 0$$
$$3x = 4 \qquad (x - 2)(x + 2) = 0$$
$$x = \frac{4}{3} \qquad\qquad x = 2, x = -2$$

The solutions shown are the only possible solutions for these two equations. No other values of x can replace the x in the equations and still result in true statements.

- Define a function in terms of the independent variable x, call that function f, and define the rule for determining the value of the dependent variable y as follows: $f(x) = 3x + 1$.

Assign a value to the independent variable, like $x = 1$, then evaluate $f(1) = 3(1) + 1 = 4 = y$.

Assign $x = 4$, $f(4) = 3(4) + 1 = 13 = y$

- We could continue to assign values to the independent variable x in this fashion and each input value would result in one corresponding (and valid) outcome.

- Each outcome is the value of the dependent variable y that the function associates with the input value of the independent variable x.

- So, when **x = 1**, the function produces an output value for the dependent variable of **y = 4**.

- When **x = 4**, the function produces an output value of the dependent variable **y = 13**.

- The value of **y** is the output that results from substituting a specified value of **x** into the function **f(x)**.

The function used in the example was expressed in functional notation. The **f(x)** is read "*f* of *x*" not "*f* times *x*." The '*f*' names the function . . . any letter, lower case or capital, can be used . . . and the *x* designates the independent variable. *To minimize confusion, when naming a function, it is a good idea to avoid lowercase letters that are often used to represent variables like **x, y, t, r**.*

3.2.1 Linear Functions

The function shown in Example 1 had a linear form. In such functions, the value of the dependent variable changes by the same fixed amount in each unit change of the independent variable (units can be time, but not necessarily so). Generally, real-world relationships that can be described by linear functions are expressed mathematically as the familiar:

$$y = f(x) = b + mx, \text{ where } m \text{ is the slope and } b \text{ is the } y \text{ coordinate of the}$$
$$y \text{ intercept } (0, b)$$

➢ **m**, is the *rate of change*. The slope is the change in the value of the dependent value, when the independent value increases by one unit.
➢ The *y intercept* is where the graph of the function passes through the *y* axis. The *y* coordinate of the *y* intercept, **b**, is the *value of dependent variable* when the value of the *independent variable is 0*.
➢ Note that the "**b + mx**" part of the function form is the linear expression form seen earlier.

EXAMPLE 5: The approximate total number of undergraduate students at James Madison University in 2010 was 17,760. That total has increased by about 350 students per year since that time and this rate of growth is expected to continue for the next few years. We wish to determine a model that would reflect the total number of undergraduate students at JMU in response to the number of years after 2010. http://research.schev.edu/iprofile.asp?UID=232423

a) Clearly identify and label the independent and dependent variables.

Independent variable: *t = number of years after 2010*

Dependent variable: *y = total number of JMU undergraduate students in t years after 2010*

b) Write the function that represents the relationship between the variables.

$$y = f(t) = \frac{350 \text{ students}}{\text{year}} \, t \text{ years} + 17{,}760 \text{ students}$$

c) Interpret the coefficients of the function.

Form of slope interpretation:

*The slope value of **[insert the value]** indicates that for each 1 **[insert independent variable unit]** increase in the **[insert the complete independent variable description]**, the **[insert the complete dependent variable description]** increases/decreases * by **[insert positive slope value]** **[insert dependent variable unit]**.*

*Choose increases for positive m, decreases for negative m.

Interpret the slope for Example 2:

The slope value of 350 indicates that for each one-year increase in the number of years after 2010, the total number of undergraduate students at JMU is expected to increase by 350 students.

Form of y intercept interpretation:

*The y coordinate of the y intercept, **[insert y coordinate value]**, is the **[insert the complete dependent variable description]** when the **[insert the complete independent variable description]** is equal to 0.*

Interpret the y intercept for Example 2:

The y coordinate of the y intercept, 17,760, is the total number of undergraduate students at JMU in 2010, when the number of years after 2010 is equal to 0.

Limitations of the model's use: It is important to realize that the accuracy of the values for the total number of undergraduate students depends on the growth rate remaining constant. It is unlikely that this rate of growth will continue indefinitely, so someone making use of the model would need to verify the growth rate value regularly.

Anytime a functional model is used, you should consider if there are limitations to its usefulness. Some functions model scientific laws and their limitations are typically well documented and presented when they are introduced. But, models that are based on narrowly defined situations such as described in most of our scenarios and much of everyday, certainly have limited usage.

YOUR TURN 3: Using the information that follows, provide the indicated information: for trips outside the city limits, the Harrisonburg Checkered Cab Company charges $3.50 and then charges an additional $2.00 per mile. Complete these steps to determine a model for the cost of a trip outside of the city limits. (Rates from Summer 2015, http://www.harrisonburgtaxi.com/)

a) Clearly identify and label the independent and dependent variables. (Notice that this is not a time-based problem.)

Independent variable:

Dependent variable:

b) Write the function that represents the relationship between the variables.

c) Interpret the coefficients of the function.

Interpret the slope:

Interpret the y intercept:

d) What would it cost to take a 20-mile trip in a Harrisonburg Checkered cab to a location outside of town?

e) What are potential limiting considerations of this model?

3.2.2   Exponential Functions

When the value of the dependent variable is described by a function with an exponential form, the value of the dependent variable changes by the same relative amount in each unit of time. Real-world growth and decay relationships that can be modelled by exponential functions are generally expressed in mathematical form as:

$$y = f(t) = A_0 (1+r)^t$$

- y is the value of dependent variable at time t
- A_0 is the initial or starting value of dependent variable at time **0**
- **1** is the decimal form of 100%, as 100% of the initial dependent variable value will be the starting place for all dependent variable growth/decay calculations.
- r is the relative change value in decimal form in each unit of time. A positive value of r indicates exponential growth; a negative value of r indicates exponential decay.
- t is the number of units of time. The units of time used in the power and associated with rate of change must be the same. For example, if the unit of time for the power is months and the rate of change is given for a year, you must convert to a common unit.
- Note that the "$A_0 \times (1+r)^t$" part of the function form is the exponential expression form.

EXAMPLE 6: According to the United Nations, the world's population was about 7.3 billion people as of mid-2015. The world population growth rate was about 1.18%. Assuming this rate of growth continues, complete these steps to determine a model for the number of people in the world in some number of years in time after 2015. https://esa.un.org/unpd/wpp/Publications/Files/Key_Findings_WPP_2015.pdf

a) Clearly identify and label the independent and dependent variables.

Independent variable: t = time in number of years after 2015

Dependent variable: y = estimated number of people in world in t years

b) Write the function that represents the relationship between the variables.

$$y = f(t) = 7.3 \times 10^9 \text{ people} (1 + 0.0118)^{t \text{ years}}$$

OR

$$y = f(t) = 7,300,000,000 \text{ people} (1 + 0.0118)^{t \text{ years}}$$

Note: the starting quantity is recorded here in scientific notation form for ease of calculation

c) What will the estimated number of people in the world by the end of 2025 (10 years) if the rate growth continues at 1.18%? Write an appropriate self-contained interpretation of the numerical result.

$$y = f(10) = 7.3 \times 10^9 \text{ people} (1+0.0118)^{10 \text{ years}} = 8,208,609,783$$

Based on the United Nations 2015 estimated world population of 7.3 billion people, we would expect there to be about 8,206,609,783 people in the world in 2025 if the current world population growth rate of 1.18% continues.

YOUR TURN 4: The new car that you just drove off the lot cost $33,543 and started depreciating in value immediately at a conservative rate of 15% per year in the first few years of ownership. This rate drops dramatically after five years, but then mileage and general wear and tear affect the value. (In reality, the first year's rate of depreciation is typically much higher.) Determine a model for the value of your car in t years after purchase (within those first five years).

a) Clearly identify and label the independent and dependent variables.

Independent variable:

Dependent variable:

b) Write the function that represents the relationship between the variables.

c) What will be the estimated value after three years? Write an appropriate self-contained interpretation of the numerical result.

d) What limit do we know exists for this model?

3.3 INTRODUCTION TO SCATTERPLOTS, CORRELATION, AND REGRESSION MODELS

Back in algebra class, when you needed to find a linear function you were given the coordinates of two points or a slope and a y intercept and you simply plugged the values into the appropriate formulas. So far in this chapter, we have focused on problems where the words allowed us to write the linear function.

Now, we consider the situation where you have many related ordered pairs and, when graphed in a scatterplot, you see a distinctive, but not perfect, linear pattern. Since all the points do not fall exactly on a line, just picking any two points to determine the function would lead to different results. Most introductory Statistics courses cover common statistical methods, called linear regression, that determine linear models that "best fit" the overall pattern observed in the scatterplot. Though those methods are beyond the scope of this book, we look at some fundamental ideas related to these statistical modelling methods. The results of these methods are closely related to the linear function models discussed in the previous section of this chapter.

The basic statistical modelling process is:

1) Data are gathered by measuring two quantitative/numerical variables on <u>each</u> individual in the studied individuals with the goal of determining how the two variables are related to each other.

   • The term "bivariate" is applied to "two-variable" data sets and analysis.

   • Prior to data collection, the individuals (the objects or people for which information will be gathered), explanatory variable (independent variable), and response variable (dependent variable) must be identified.

   • The use of the terms *explanatory* and *response* do not imply any cause and effect relationship.

2) The resulting bivariate data, (ordered pairs), are graphed on a **scatterplot**, with the explanatory variable on the x axis and the response variable on the y axis. This is so the association or relationship between the two quantitative variables can be observed and analyzed.

3) A complete graphical analysis of the relationship/association seen in the scatterplot is performed.

4) If the pattern seen in the scatterplot suggests that the association/relationship is linear, then the linear numerical analysis is performed to find the model and correlation coefficient. *In this book, these numerical details will be provided in the problem or determined by built-in calculator functions of data.*

5) The coefficients are contextually interpreted to provide insight to the numerical association between the variables.

Note that there are two distinct analyses in this process . . . a graphical analysis and a numerical analysis. Though it is tempting to immediately jump to the numerical analysis, doing so can result in poor decisions.

Before beginning the analyses, it is worth noting that once the real-life association between two variables is carefully considered, it is often obvious which variable should be "explanatory" and which a "response." At other times, we may know the variables are related but a logical determination of explanatory and response is much tougher. Consider the variables *weight, measured in pounds,* and *height, measured in feet,* measured on a group of children from an elementary school. Obviously, in this group, both height and weight are related to a third variable, the age of the child . . . the kindergarteners and first graders will tend to be shorter and have lower weights than the fifth graders. When the two variables are considered for such a group of children, it seems quite logical that height would be the explanatory variable and weight the response variable. Think about seeing the group of elementary school students in the gymnasium. If you were wanting to guess the grade level of the children simply by looking, what would you consider? If the children were standing around, height seems a good response! In children of widely varying grade level, height almost becomes a substitute for the variable "age" and logically helps "explain" a lot of things, such as weight, size of vocabulary, and shoe size. However, this does not mean that height causes things like size of the vocabulary.

YOUR TURN 5: The pair of variables has a correlation coefficient value indicating a "strong correlation" (and the scatterplot indicate a linear association).

The size of the building on fire and the number of firefighters called to fight the fire for all the fires in Harrisonburg in the last year.

Discuss the following, including an explanation of your reasoning:

1) Who/what are the individuals?

2) Which variable, if any, might be a more appropriate "explanatory" or "predictive" variable? Explain your reasoning. (Remember that "cause" is not necessary for an explanatory variable to have predictive value for the response.)

3) Would the trend be expected to be positive or negative? Explain.

4) Is there likely to be some "causal" impact of the explanatory variable on the response? Or are both variables related to some common cause (identify that common cause/confounding variable)? Or is it some combination?

3.3.1 Graphical Analysis of Bivariate/Two-Variable Data

EXAMPLE 7: The scatterplot below shows how the six-year graduation rate responds to the estimated median SAT score for 52 US public universities with student populations of 15,000 to 20,000 students in 2007. The data represent only those public institutions reported by The Education Trust.

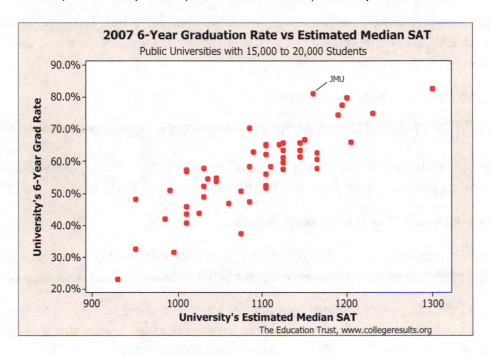

1) What are the individuals (from opening description)?

   The individuals are the 52 US public universities with student population sizes between 15,000 and 20,000 in 2007, as reported by The Education Trust.

2) What is the explanatory variable (from opening description, the variable is always defined for one individual)?

   The explanatory variable is a university's estimated median SAT score.

3) What is the response variable (from opening description, the variable is always defined for one individual)?

   The response variable is a university's six-year graduation rate, in percent.

   HINT: As you describe each of the items that follow, imagine that you are speaking to someone that is not looking at the scatterplot!

---

4) Discuss the direction of the trend observed

- Determine if the trend is negative or positive

- Explain how the values of response variables tend to be associated with values of the explanatory variable

The relationship between the variables is positive indicating that low graduation rates are associated with lower median SAT scores and higher graduation rates are associated with higher median SAT scores.

5) Discuss the form of the observed pattern

- Is it fundamentally linear, curved, or is there no obvious pattern?

- Order of discussion is important; you are describing how the response variable values respond as the explanatory variable increases (goes from small to larger values).

- Provide intervals of values for each variable.

- If there are obvious gaps that result in clusters of ordered pairs that look like separate groups of information, discuss each cluster separately.

The association between six-year graduation rates and median SAT scores for these 52 universities is fairly linear with the graduation rates spreading from about 22% to just above 80% as the median SAT scores spread from about 930 to 1300.

6) Discuss the strength of the observed association

- Strong—overall the points form a nearly perfect imaginary line or curve

- Weak—overall the points are so widely scattered that a line or curved pattern is difficult to see

- Moderately strong—the line or curved pattern is distinctive but there is quite a bit of up and down spread (similar values of x have y values that vary quite a bit). Provide at least one illustrative example of where the independent variable values are similar, but the dependent variable values are very different.

The strength of the association between the graduation rates and median SAT scores is moderately strong because universities with similar median SAT scores have graduation rates that vary quite a lot. For example, several of the universities have median SAT scores that appear to be within 10 points of 1000, but the six-year graduation rates vary from about 30% up to just below 60%, a nearly 30 percentage point difference.

7) Discuss outliers, (*ordered pairs that obviously behave differently than the pattern seen in most of the data*)

- Observations that are outliers in the **x** direction may occur at either extreme of the explanatory variable's values. Ask yourself if the minimum value of **x** seems much smaller or if the maximum value of **x** seems much larger than most of the other values.

- Observations that are outliers in the **y** direction are ordered pairs that are further from an imaginary line through the data in a vertical up/down direction than what is typical with the other ordered pairs. These outliers can appear among any of the ordered pair.

The highest median SAT score of about 1300 is about 75 points higher than the next highest score, a gap that separates it from most of the data in the x direction. It looks like that university may have a slightly lower six-year graduation rate than the trend seen in the data would suggest. JMU appears to be a slight outlier in the y direction as its six-year graduation rate, just above 80%, appears to be the highest among all of these universities including several with higher median SAT scores.

YOUR TURN 6: The scatterplot below shows how the exam 2 scores responded to the exam 1 scores for 23 students in a Statistics class.

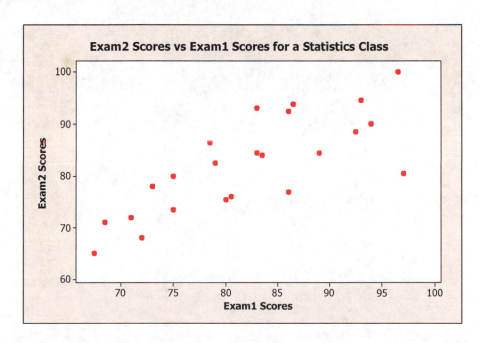

a) What are the individuals?

b) What is the explanatory variable (define for one individual)?

c) What is the response variable (define for one individual)?

HINT: As you describe each of the items that follow, imagine that you are speaking to someone that is not looking at the scatterplot!

d) Discuss the direction of the trend observed

e) Discuss the form of the observed pattern

f) Discuss the strength of the observed association

g) Discuss outliers

3.3.2 Numerical Analysis of Bivariate/Two-Variable Data

If the association observed between the two quantitative variables on the scatterplot is linear, then we can summarize the association numerically with correlation coefficient, *r*, which measures the direction and strength of the linear association between two quantitative variables. You must be very cautious in using *r* if you have not first analyzed the scatterplot. Calculators and computer programs have no way of determining when such calculations are appropriate and will always calculate its value when requested, if the input form is correct. For data with strong outliers and nonlinear associations, those calculated correlation values may appear to be those we would expect to be associated with linear associations. It is up to us to know when it is appropriate to use this measurement and when it is not. The formula used to find this measurement is not included in the book as the information will either be provided, or you will use built-in functionality of calculators to find them.

Characteristics of correlation coefficient values (when appropriately applied) are the following:

➤ Correlation coefficient values are a scale with values between −1 and 1
➤ Positive correlation coefficient values are associated with linear associations with positive trends
➤ Negative correlation coefficient values are associated with linear associations with negative trends
➤ Perfect linear associations have *r* values of 1 (if trend is positive) and −1 (if trend is negative)
➤ Though the **scale** uses decimal values, they are NEVER expressed as percentages
➤ Values of *r* have no units; the units of measure in the data (as long as consistent) do not impact the values of *r*
➤ Values of *r* close to 0, imply very weak linear associations; an *r* = **0** would indicate no linear association (but would not imply that there was not some other clear pattern)

- Though what is considered weak, moderate or strong varies in real-life application, often by field, we will use the following rules of thumb for appropriately applied correlation coefficients:
  - $-0.5 < r < 0.5$, implies weak linear association . . . the closer to 0, the weaker the linear association

  - $-0.8 < r < -0.5$ AND $0.5 < r < 0.8$, implies moderate linear association. However, keep in mind that values near −0.8 or 0.8 are stronger than those near −0.5 or 0.5

  - $-0.9 \leq r \leq -0.8$ AND $0.8 \leq r \leq 0.9$, implies strong linear association

  - $-1 \leq r < -0.9$ AND $0.9 < r \leq 1$, implies very strong linear association

- Correlation, even if very strong, **never** implies a cause and effect association

If the association observed between the variables on the scatterplot is linear, we can use regression to model that relationship. The **equation of the least-squares regression line** for predicting **y** from **x** is

$$\hat{y} = b_0 + b_1 x$$

*Where $\hat{y}$ indicates a predicted model for the response variable **y**, where b_1 is the slope and b_0 is the **y** intercept value. This is essentially the form we saw for linear functions, using a different notation and order.*

The formulas used to find the coefficients are not included here because the information will either be provided, or you will use built-in functionality of calculators to find them. The model coefficients (the slope and *y* intercept) are interpreted in essentially the same ways that they were interpreted in Section 3.3.1.

EXAMPLE 8: The numerical analysis of how the 2007 six-year graduation rates responded to the estimated median SAT scores at the 52 US public universities with student population sizes of 15,000 to 20,000 is considered. The data represent only those public institutions reported by The Education Trust.

Since the association between the 2007 six-year graduation rate and the estimated median SAT score at the 52 US public universities with student population sizes of 15,000 to 20,000 was clearly linear it is appropriate to complete the numerical analysis. Minitab 16 provided the following numerical output.

$$r = 0.836 \quad \hat{y} = -91.6 + 0.136x$$

From Example 1a, the independent variable is a university's estimated median SAT score and the dependent variable is a university's six-year graduation rate, in percent.

Interpret the correlation coefficient:

The correlation coefficient of 0.836 indicates a strong positive linear association between the universities' estimated median SAT scores and the universities' six-year graduation rates.

Look back at Example 7 and determine if this correlation coefficient interpretation supports was stated about the trend, direction, and strength in the graphical analysis of the same data.

Interpret the slope:

The slope value of 0.136 indicates that for each one-point increase in the university's estimated median SAT score, the university's six-year graduation rate "is expected to increase" by 0.136 percentage points.

This slope interpretation is essentially the same interpretation as seen earlier in the chapter, but there is a subtle difference in wording in discussing this "predicted" slope, note the underlined information that reflects that the "hypothetical" nature of the predicted model.

Interpret the *y* intercept:

The y coordinate of the y intercept, −91.6, is the university's estimated six-year graduation rate, in percent, when the university's estimated median SAT score is 0. In this case, a literal interpretation does not make sense because a graduation rate cannot be negative. (If an interpretation clearly does not make "real world sense," the inclusion of a second sentence that explains that should be included.)

YOUR TURN 7: The numerical analysis of how the exam 2 scores responded to the exam 1 scores for 23 students in a Statistics class is considered. Since the association seen in the earlier scatterplot between the exam 2 scores and exam 1 scores is linear, it is appropriate to complete the numerical analysis. Minitab 16 provided the following numerical output.

$$r = 0.776 \quad \hat{y} = 15.5 + 0.811x$$

Independent variable

Dependent variable

Interpret the correlation coefficient:

Consider: Does this go along with what was stated about the trend, direction, and strength in the graphical analysis? Could you explain your reasoning?

Interpret the slope (use the form from earlier in the chapter):

Interpret the *y* intercept (use the form from earlier in the chapter):

EXAMPLE 9: One famous example that shows the importance of graphing before using correlation coefficients and linear models was published back in 1973. The article presented four data sets that are now known as the "Anscombe Quartet." *Anscombe's Quartet (F.J. Anscombe, "Graphs in Statistical Analysis," American Statistician, 27 [February 1973], 17–21). Here are the data sets:*

X1	Y1	X2	Y2	X3	Y3	X4	Y4
10	8.04	10	9.14	10	7.46	8	6.58
8	6.95	8	8.14	8	6.77	8	5.76
13	7.58	13	8.74	13	12.74	8	7.71
9	8.81	9	8.77	9	7.11	8	8.84
11	8.33	11	9.26	11	7.81	8	8.47
14	9.96	14	8.1	14	8.84	8	7.04
6	7.24	6	6.13	6	6.08	8	5.25
4	4.26	4	3.1	4	5.39	19	12.5
12	10.84	12	9.13	12	8.15	8	5.56
7	4.82	7	7.26	7	6.42	8	7.91
5	5.68	5	4.74	5	5.73	8	6.8

When the correlation coefficients and the predicted equations were calculated for each pair of variables, these were the results:

Variable Pair	Correlation Coefficient	Model
X1,Y1	$r = 0.816$	$\hat{Y}1 \approx 3 + 0.5\ X1$
X2,Y2	$r = 0.816$	$\hat{Y}2 \approx 3 + 0.5\ X2$
X3,Y3	$r = 0.816$	$\hat{Y}3 \approx 3 + 0.5\ X3$
X4,Y4	$r = 0.817$	$\hat{Y}4 \approx 3 + 0.5\ X4$

YOUR TURN 8a: What do the correlation coefficients suggest about the relationship between each *x* variable and *y*?

One might easily jump to the conclusion that the associations in each set are the same, or at least very similar when looking only at the numerical results. However, a quick look at the scatterplots, shown in the graphic below, clearly indicates very different association patterns. The X1, Y1 pair is the only set of the four that can appropriately use the calculated correlation coefficient and model. Failure to graph can lead to misuse of the statistical tools and result in poor decisions!

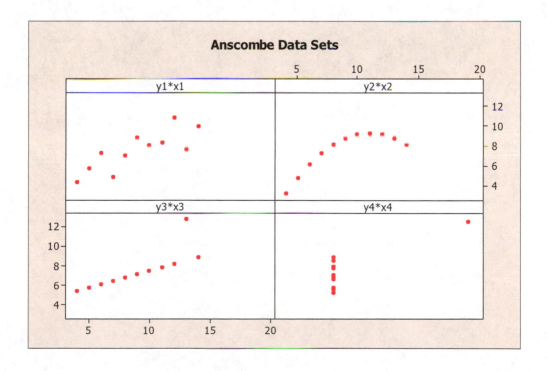

Anscombe Data Sets

YOUR TURN FINAL ANSWERS

Section 3.1

1) a) absolute change = $4,224 - $3,930 = $294

   James Madison University's in-state tuition per semester in the fall 2011 was $294 higher than its $3,930 per semester in-state tuition in fall 2010.

   b) $4,224 + \dfrac{\$294}{\text{year}}\left(5 \text{ years}\right) = \$5,694$

   c) $4,224 + \dfrac{\$294}{\text{year}}\left(t \text{ years}\right)$

   d) relative change = $\dfrac{\$4,224 - \$3,930}{\$3,930} \approx 0.0748,\ 7.48\%$

   James Madison University's in-state tuition per semester in the fall 2011 was about 7.48% higher than its $3,930 per semester in-state tuition in fall 2010.

   e) $\$4,224\left(1+.0748\right)^{5} \approx \$6,058.46$

   f) $\$4,224\left(1+.0748\right)^{t \text{ years}}$

2) a/b

Square ID Number	1	2	3	4	5	. . .n
Number of grains on square	1	2	4	8	16	Depends on n
Number of grains on square as power of 2	2^0	2^1	2^2	2^3	2^4	2^{n-1}
Total number of grains on board as of square id number	1 2^1-1	3 2^2-1	7 2^3-1	15 2^4-1	31 2^5-1	2^n-1

   c) Number of grains on square 20: $2^{20-1} = 2^{19} = 524,288$

   Total number of grains up to and including square 20: $2^{20} - 1 = 1,048,576 - 1 = 1,048,575$

d) Approximate weight of rice grains on the board up to and including square 20:

$$1,048,575 \text{ rice grains} \times \frac{1 \text{ pound}}{29,000 \text{ rice grains}} = 36.1578 \text{ pounds}$$

Section 3.2

3) a) **Independent variable: x** = number of miles traveled in the trip outside city limits

Dependent variable: y = cost of Harrisonburg Cab trip outside the city limits

b) $y = f(x) = \dfrac{\$2}{\text{mile}} x \text{ miles} + \$3.50$

c) The slope value of 2 indicates that for each 1-mile increase in the number of miles traveled in a trip outside city limits, the cost of a Harrisonburg Cab trip outside the city limits increases by $2.

The y coordinate of the y intercept, 3.50, is the cost of a Harrisonburg Cab trip outside the city limits when the number of miles traveled in the trip outside city limits is equal to 0.

d) $y = f(20) = \dfrac{\$2}{\text{mile}} (20 \text{ miles}) + \$3.50 = \$43.50$

e) Potential limitations are things like the cab company's distance limits that they are willing to travel outside the city or changes to their cost structure.

4) a) **Independent variable: t** = number of years after vehicle purchase

Dependent variable: y = value of vehicle in t years after purchase

b) $y = f(t) = \$33,543 (1 - 0.15)^{t \text{ years}}$

c) $y = f(t) = \$33,543 (1 - 0.15)^{3 \text{ years}} \approx \$20,599.59$

At a 15% rate of depreciation, the estimated value of a vehicle purchased for $33,543 will be about $20,599.59 after three years.

d) We know that this model is only appropriate for the first five years after the vehicle is purchased.

Section 3.3

5) a) The individuals are all of the fires in Harrisonburg in the last year; the size of the building on fire and the number of firefighters called to fight the fire are measured for each fire.

b) The explanatory variable is size of the building on fire. Number of fire fighters is not going to impact building size but the size of the building on fire would logically impact the number of firefighters needed.

c) The direction of the association between the variables is positive. Small buildings on fire would need a smaller number of firefighters and larger buildings on fire would need a larger number of fire fighters.

d) The size of the building on fire is going to have a causal impact on the number of firefighters at the fire because, as noted in part c, larger buildings on fire need more firefighters to fight the fire than smaller buildings on fire would need.

6) a) The individuals are the 23 students in the Statistics class.

b) The explanatory variable is a student's exam 1 score. (Recall: variables are defined for 1 individual.

c) The response variable is a student's exam 2 score.

d) The relationship between the variables is positive indicating that low exam 2 scores are associated with low exam 1 scores and high exam 2 scores are associated with high exam 1 scores.

e) The association between exam 2 scores and exam 1 scores for the 23 students in the Statistics class is linear with the exam 2 scores spreading from about 65 to 100 as the exam 1 scores spread from about 63 to 95.

f) The strength of the association between exam 2 scores and exam 1 scores is moderately strong because students with similar exam 1 scores have exam 2 scores that vary quite a lot. For example, several students have exam 1 scores around 85 but the exam 2 scores for those students vary from about 65 up to just below 93, a 28-point difference.

g) One student appears to be an outlier in the y direction. They had a very high exam 1 score of about 97 but their exam 2 score was only about 80, much lower than the pattern would suggest that the exam 2 score would be.

7) **Independent variable: x** = a student's exam 1 score

Dependent variable: y = a student's exam 2 score

The correlation coefficient of 0.776 indicates a moderate positive linear association between the students' exam 1 and exam 2 scores.

The slope value of 0.811 indicates that for each 1-point increase in the student's exam 1 score, the student's exam 2 score tended to increase by 0.811 points.

The y coordinate of the y intercept, 15.5, is the estimated student's exam 2 score, when the student's exam 1 score is 0.

8) a) The 0.816/0.817 correlation coefficients suggest strong positive linear relationships between each x variable and y.

b) The upper left scatterplot shows a moderately scattered linear association with no outliers. The upper right scatterplot shows a very strong (perfect) curvilinear association with no outliers. Correlation coefficients do not quantify the strength of curved relationships, no matter how perfect.

The lower left scatterplot shows a nearly perfect linear association with outlier in the y direction. The outlier makes the association look weaker than it really is.

The lower right scatterplot shows a nearly perfect vertical line with a strong outlier in the x direction on the right. Correlation coefficients, like linear functions, cannot be calculated for vertical lines. The linear equation and correlation coefficient provided for this final scatterplot could only be calculated because of the outlier.

CHECK YOUR MASTERY

➤ **Chapter Terminology:** *If you do not know the meaning, record it here.*

Numerical Expression

Algebraic Expression

Linear Growth/Decay

Exponential Growth/Decay

Independent Variable

Dependent Variable

Function

Slope

Y Coordinate

Y Intercept

Individuals

Response Variable

Explanatory Variable

Association

Scatterplot

Trend

Outlier

Correlation Coefficient

Regression Equation

➢ **Do you know:**

- The form of linear and exponential expressions?

- How to label and describe variables?

- The form of linear and exponential functions?

- When to use percentage points?

- The correlation coefficient strength guidelines?

- How to describe the characteristics of association/relationship based on a scatterplot?

- The required language for interpretations: slope, y intercept, and correlation coefficient?

➢ **Can you:**

- Write numerical and algebraic expressions for linear growth/decay and then evaluate for indicated values?

- Write numerical and algebraic expressions for exponential growth/decay? and then evaluate for indicated values?

- Identify and label independent and dependent variables?

- Write linear functions and then evaluate for indicated values?

- Interpret slopes and y coordinates of the y intercept in the forms indicated and in context?

- Write exponential functions and then evaluate for indicated values?

- Determine the individuals and determine which of the stated variables is the more reasonable explanatory variable?

- Complete the seven steps of the scatterplot graphical analysis?

- Interpret the correlation coefficient in context?

EXERCISES

Do not forget to report decimal answers to the nearest ten-thousandths and percentages to nearest hundredths. Self-contained responses convey full contextual details so that reader knowledge of the question and calculations is unnecessary.

I) Write the appropriate numerical or algebraic expression, as indicated, that mathematically represents the described linear or exponential situation. *Remember that expressions are one sided.* Do not forget units in the expressions and in numerical expression answers.

1) Ralph would like to lose a few pounds before his best friend's wedding. He currently weighs 200 pounds and plans on losing 2 pounds per week. Assuming he sticks to his plan, what should he weigh when he attends the wedding in 12 weeks? Provide the numerical expression and answer.

   Then write the algebraic expression that describes Ralph's weight after t weeks.

2) The current price of regular grade gasoline is $2.89 per gallon and has been rising about 5 cents per week for some time. If this weekly increase remains at 5 cents, what will the per gallon price of regular grade gasoline be in eight weeks? Provide the numerical expression and answer. Then write the algebraic expression that describes the per gallon price of regular grade gasoline after t weeks.

3) According to the US Department of Agriculture (USDA), the average price of that one-pound T-bone steak you planned on serving Dad for his birthday is $7.86. Beef prices have recently averaged a 0.2% decrease in price each month. If this monthly trend in beef prices continues, what would a one-pound T-bone steak cost in six months? Provide the numerical expression and answer. Then write the algebraic expression that describes the price in t months.

4) Supermarket food prices are expected to rise about 0.2% each month. If a family currently spends about $435 each month, what will their monthly food costs be in eight months? Provide the numerical expression and answer. Then write the algebraic expression that describes the monthly food costs in t months.

II) Each of the following problems requires a linear or exponential model. For each one:

- Label and fully describe the independent and dependent variables.

- Write the appropriate model in function form.

- If the model is linear, interpret both the slope and y intercept as described in the examples.

- Complete any other work indicated in the problem.

- Remember units in work and answers!

5) The US population as of the end of 2014 was about 323 million people. The yearly rate of growth at that time in the US population was about 0.8%. Label and describe the independent and dependent variables and provide the model to estimate the number of people in the United States in t years after 2014. Then use the model to estimate the number of people in the United States after 10 years. Write an appropriate self-contained sentence for a reader without access to the information in the question.

6) Germany's population in 2014 was about 81 million people and, according to the CIA World Fact book, was declining at a yearly rate of 0.18%. Label and describe the independent and dependent variables and provide the model to estimate the number of people in Germany in t years after 2014. Then use the model to estimate the number of people in Germany after 10 years. Write an appropriate self-contained sentence for a reader without access to the information in the question.

7) A patient takes an 800 mg dose of acetaminophen as prescribed by his physician. Acetaminophen is eliminated from the body at a rate of 28% per hour. Label and describe the independent and dependent variables and provide the model to estimate the quantity of acetaminophen remaining in the patient's body after t hours. How much acetaminophen will remain in the patient's body after 4 hours? Write an appropriate self-contained sentence for a reader without access to the information in the question.

8) For trips within the city, the charges posted on the Harrisonburg Checkered Cab Company website in July 2015 indicated the following: $3.50 plus $1.80 per mile. Label and describe the independent and dependent variables and provide the model to estimate the cost of an in-city cab ride travelling x miles. What would a 2.8 miles trip in one of this company's vehicles cost? Complete all steps listed in the instructions.

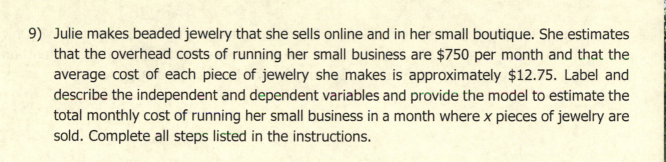

9) Julie makes beaded jewelry that she sells online and in her small boutique. She estimates that the overhead costs of running her small business are $750 per month and that the average cost of each piece of jewelry she makes is approximately $12.75. Label and describe the independent and dependent variables and provide the model to estimate the total monthly cost of running her small business in a month where x pieces of jewelry are sold. Complete all steps listed in the instructions.

10) Recall Julie's jewelry business from the previous question.
   a) She sells her beaded jewelry at an average price of $75. Label and describe the independent and dependent variables and provide the model to estimate the total monthly revenue in a month where x pieces of jewelry are sold. Complete all steps listed in the instructions.

b) How many pieces of jewelry does Julie need to sell in a month to break even? (Only after she meets her expenses does she start to see a profit!) Set the cost function from problem 9 equal to the revenue function in part a and solve for x.

11) According to their website, the basic cost to rent a 24-foot U-Haul truck is $39.95 plus $1.29 per mile. Label and describe the independent and dependent variables and provide the model to estimate the cost of renting the truck for a move to some location x miles away. (Obviously, it will be much higher with insurance, tax, moving equipment, etc.) What is the basic truck rental cost for a move to a location that is 250 miles away? Complete all steps listed in the instructions.

III) Each of these pairs of variables has a correlation coefficient value indicating a "strong correlation" (and the scatterplots indicate a linear association). Discuss each pair, including an explanation of your reasoning, as you consider:

a) Who/what are the individuals?

b) Which variable, if any, might be a more appropriate "explanatory" or "predictive" variable? Explain your reasoning. (Remember that "cause" is not necessary for an explanatory variable to have predictive value for the response.)

c) Would the trend be expected to be positive or negative? Explain.

d) Is there likely to be some "causal" impact of the explanatory variable on the response? Or are both variables related to some common cause (identify that common cause/confounding variable)? Or is it some combination?

12) GPA and time spent on social media while studying or doing homework, reported for many college students

13) Number of emergency personnel at an accident and extent of injuries of those in the accident, reported for many car accidents

14) Cost of corn and cost of beef production, measured over many years

IV) *Bivariate Analysis*

Part 1: Complete the graphical analysis of the bivariate data by responding to each of the following in complete sentences and in context as illustrated in the chapter. *Remember that for full context the variables' and individuals' descriptions are based on opening information, not only on the axis label.*

   a) What are the individuals? Be specific!
   b) What is the explanatory variable? Be specific!
   c) What is the response variable? Be specific!
   d) Discuss the direction of the trend observed.
   e) Discuss the form of the observed pattern.
   f) Discuss the strength of the observed association.
   g) Discuss outliers.

Part 2: Interpret the slope, *y* intercept and correlation coefficient in context, as illustrated in the chapter, when provided.

15) The scatterplot below shows how the percentages of each state's population with home access to high-speed internet responded to the percentages of each state's population that were living in poverty for all 50 states and the District of Columbia in 2014. The data are from the US Census Bureau.

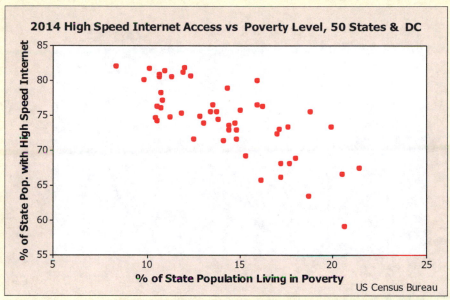

The numerical results are provided for contextual interpretation.

$$\hat{y} = 91.2 - 1.18x \quad r = -0.743$$

16) The scatterplot below shows how the Average Live Births per Woman responds to the Number of Infant Deaths per 1000 Live Births from 2010 to 2015 for 273 Countries. The data are from UN data, a service of the United Nations (http://data.un.org/).

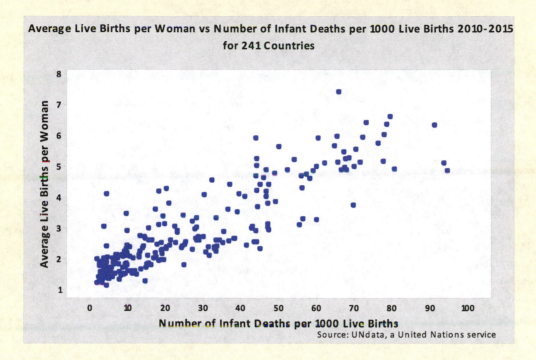

Average Live Births per Woman vs Number of Infant Deaths per 1000 Live Births 2010-2015 for 241 Countries

Source: UNdata, a United Nations service

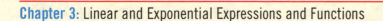

The numerical results are provided for contextual interpretation.

$$\hat{y} = 1.452 + 0.053x \quad r = 0.8785$$

CHAPTER 4
Introduction to Data and Data Analysis

CHAPTER OBJECTIVES

Upon completion of this chapter, the student should be able to

☐ Identify and describe the individuals and the variable from a scenario description, then identify the appropriate graph type.

☐ Write the complete self-contained contextual description of a univariate variable distribution when the graph is provided; based on this analysis, identify and justify the use of the appropriate set of number summaries.

☐ Demonstrate the ability to find the five-number summary, including ordered positions both manually. Find and report values of number summaries from calculator output.

☐ Determine and report the approximate percentages of observations in intervals of variable values based on the empirical rule.

☐ Demonstrate the ability to complete all steps in a normal probability calculation requiring the use of the standard normal table, using proper notation throughout.

☐ Write complete self-contained contextual interpretations in proportion, probability, and percentage forms for the results of normal probability calculations.

By the time a person begins college, they have experienced at least some very basic introduction to *Statistics*. Though some will have taken an entire introductory Statistics course that integrated the mathematical aspects with communication and meaning, most have encountered the subject primarily as a set of formulas and calculations. Though accuracy of numerical results is certainly desirable, in this age where $20 calculators easily produce accurate numerical results with little more effort than entering "data values" into a list, "arriving" at the correct "number" is no longer an adequate introduction to the powerful tools that the field of *Statistics* offers to the educated world citizen.

4.1 WHAT IS STATISTICS? BASIC STATISTICAL TERMINOLOGY AND DEFINITIONS

➢ **Statistics** is the science of collecting, organizing, and interpreting data.

➢ **Data** are contextual facts and numerical information from which conclusions are drawn. **Data set** is a generic phrase used to refer to the raw collection of facts and numbers that we have about a specific topic of interest for specific group of individuals.

➢ An **individual** (also called **subject** or **case**) is one of the "objects" or "entities" to be studied. An individual might be a person or animal but could also be an entity like a part coming off an assembly line, a city, a country, a state, and so forth.

➢ A **population** is the complete set of individuals of interest. It is the entire group of individuals for which information is desired or needed. It is typically impossible, or at the very least impractical, to gather information for the entire population.

➢ The **sample** is the subset of individuals from the population for which information is actually gathered. The **sample size** is simply the number of individuals in the sample.

➢ A **variable** is a characteristic that is measured or recorded for one individual. A variable is always defined at the individual level. Variables can be either *qualitative/categorical* (gender, race, locality, educational attainment, etc.) or *quantitative* (age, number of children, weight, etc.)

➢ The **distribution** of a variable is some presentation of information that shows the values that a variable can take and the frequency (or relative frequency) of those values. For a qualitative variable, the "values" are the categories of the variable. Tables, graphs, and functions are all potential forms of distribution presentation.

4.2 LOOKING AT VARIABLE BEHAVIOR—GRAPHICAL APPROACH TO DESCRIBING A VARIABLE'S DISTRIBUTION

Once data have been gathered and, typically, entered into a computer file, the next step is to get the data into organized forms that allow patterns and exceptions to be easily identified. The most common forms of organization are tables and graphs, which vary in type depending on whether the variable to be analyzed is qualitative or quantitative. As with interpretive sentences, communication is a key consideration in presenting meaningful tables and graphs; precise labelling is the best way to be certain the results are meaningful to readers. Once again ask yourself "Does this table/graph make sense if it is all the information available to the reader?" before moving to the next task.

4.2.1 Organizing Qualitative Variable Data

Frequency tables are used to organize and display the distributions of both qualitative and quantitative variables, though visually they look a bit different. Labelling should identify the contextual detail necessary to allow the reader to understand the information as well as to judge the adequacy of the information for making decisions related to the topic. Key information to be included whenever possible: data source, time frame, individuals, and variable description including units and categories.

EXAMPLE 1a: The title of the frequency table indicates that the variable is the level of education attained by a person of age 25 years or older and, since this is US Census Bureau data, the individuals are all people in the United States aged 25 and older as of 2013.

Educational Attainment in the US Age 25 Years and Over, 2013		
	(Numbers in thousands)	%
Less than high school	24,517	11.84974
High School Graduate	61,704	29.82325
Some college (no degree)	34,805	16.82222
Associate's degree	20,367	9.843934
Bachelor's degree	41,575	20.09435
Master's degree	17,395	8.407484
Professional degree	3,066	1.481882
Doctoral degree	3,470	1.677147
Total	206,899	100

US Census Bureau

The first column indicates the categories of the variable, which are the variable values. The second column gives the number (frequency) of individuals in each category and the third column is the relative frequency within each category in percent form. (Divide each entry by total and convert to a percentage.)

Note the full context labelling of this table. When you label tables and graphs, always ask yourself "Can this table/graph be fully understood without reading any other information?" Notice the "(Numbers in thousands)." This means that each value in the column has 3 more zeros. Thus when we see the 24,517 value, the table is indicating that in 2013 there were 24,517,000 people in the US who were 25 years of age or older with less than a high school education.

The two primary graphical tools for displaying distributions of qualitative data are bar charts and pie charts. Pie charts are used to display relative frequency information but can be used only in situations where all possible categories of the variable are represented, where each individual's value falls into exactly one category (there are NO overlaps), and where the data represents a common whole. Pie charts are less effective when some categories make up very small percentages of the whole, when the chart is presented without color and/or when the categories have similar percentages; in each of these situations, the details of each category may be very difficult to discern. Bar charts, on the other hand, are much more flexible in that they can be employed even when only some categories are studied and when individuals fall into multiple categories. Pie charts have limited usage in serious statistical analysis.

For example, imagine the results of a survey on drug use where the variable is the "drug used." In this situation, it is very likely that some individuals would indicate use of multiple drugs among selections of cigarettes, alcohol, marijuana, prescription drugs, cocaine, and other. Pie charts are not appropriate in this situation, but bar chart use is appropriate. Consider a situation where there is a desire to have a graphical view of the similarities/differences in either the number of or percentage of people in each of the **degree-earning** categories of the educational attainment table. Again, bar chart usage is appropriate directly from the table, but that is not the case for a pie chart. By only looking at the degree-earning categories, the "whole" is no longer represented, thus the pie chart cannot be used.

EXAMPLE 1b: The pie chart displays the distribution of educational attainment of age 25 and older individuals in the United States in 2013.

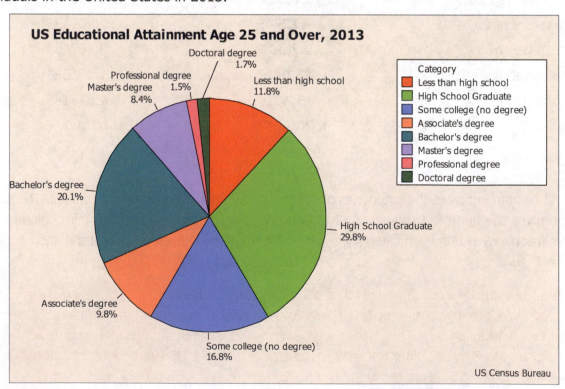

QUANTITATIVE LITERACY AND REASONING

Pie chart usage, with the percentage of individuals in each category, is appropriate with this data because the available data represent all possible categories of education attainment and each 25 or older person fits into exactly one category. As Census data, the data represent the "whole" of all people in the United States aged 25 and older as of 2013.

The corresponding bar chart follows. Bar charts have two axes, a variable axis, which is labelled with the categories of the qualitative variable, and the frequency/relative frequency axis. The frequency/relative frequency axis should, with few exceptions, start at zero. Each variable value, a category, is represented by a bar. All bars are of the same width, with bar heights changing in response to frequency or relative frequency in the category. The bars of a bar chart do NOT touch and equal-size spaces between bars are required.

EXAMPLE 1c: The bar chart displaying the distribution of educational attainment of age 25 and older individuals in the United States in 2013 is shown.

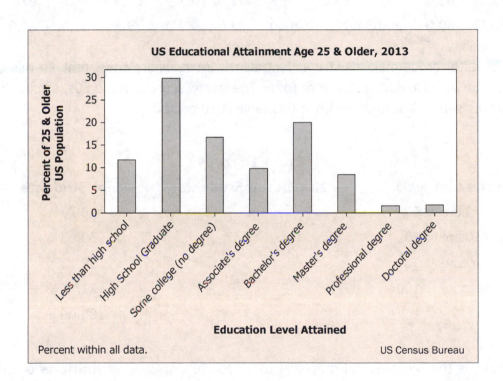

In this bar chart, the percentage values, (relative frequencies), are represented on the vertical axis, though the number of individuals in each category could have been used.

The variable axis, shown horizontally, has a "scale" that is the variable values, which are the category descriptions.

4.2.2 Organizing Quantitative Variable Data

Frequency tables for quantitative variables are different from those for a qualitative variable in that we must group by similar values rather than by a common category. Each grouping is called a **class** and the **class width** is measured from the beginning of one class to the beginning of the next class. Classes must be defined so that each value fits into exactly one class. When possible, create classes that people will find easy to understand. Classes that easily allow counting by 5, 10, 20, and so forth, make sense, while starting with a 17 and counting by 3.5 would likely be confusing. If your data have groupings that are commonly used, use those for your classes.

EXAMPLE 2: The following data represent all of the exam 1 scores for students in a class. Assume that these scores are the earned "points."

| 93.0 | 71.0 | 86.0 | 86.5 | 68.5 | 80.5 | 72.0 | 67.5 | 83.5 | 94.0 | 92.5 | 75.0 |
| 79.0 | 96.5 | 80.0 | 73.0 | 75.0 | 97.0 | 83.0 | 89.0 | 78.5 | 83.0 | 86.0 | |

Grouping by letter grade makes sense as long as the intervals are consistent. In this course, 90 and above is an A, 80 to 89.9 a B, and so forth. The lowest score is in the 60s, so counting by 10s from 60 makes sense. The class width in this table is 10 points.

Grade Classes	Exam 1 Scores	
	Number of Students	**% of Students**
60 ≤ score < 70	2	8.70%
70 ≤ score < 80	7	30.43%
80 ≤ score < 90	9	39.13%
90 ≤ score < 100	5	21.74%
Total	23	100.00%

A **histogram** is the most typical graphical tool used to display **distributions** of quantitative variables. As usual, labelling that allows the graph to stand on its own is critical. Like bar charts, histograms use the heights of equal width bars to convey the "number of" or "relative frequency" of individuals in each class. This axis should, with few exceptions, start at zero. The two graphs are otherwise very different tools. The variable axis is a continuous numerical scale that should start at some reasonable value slightly below but near the lowest observation value. Rarely does it make sense for the variable axis to start at zero. The bars of a histogram always touch except when a gap exists because a class has zero individuals. The histogram that matches the *exam 1* frequency table follows.

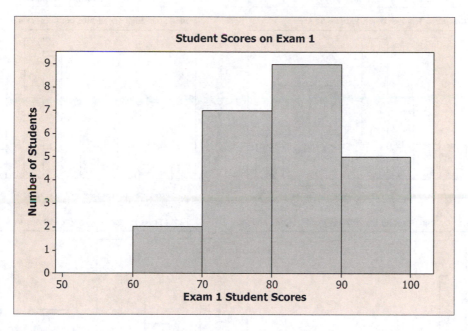

4.2.3 Describing the Distribution of a Quantitative Variable from Its Histogram

Use a histogram to observe and describe the behavior of a quantitative variable distribution. Writing self-contained contextual descriptions of a variable's behavior based on the histogram not only helps develop communication skills, but also improves analysis skills by encouraging you to pay attention to details. *The variable behavior discussion is based entirely on what can be determined from the histogram (rather than calculations based on the raw data values).*

➢ Start with precise descriptions of the variable and the individuals based on the accompanying information provided in the problem. Be sure to decide and explain whether the data represent a sample or a population.
➢ Next, give a contextual description of distribution. This basic shape information includes a determination of left skew, right skew, or symmetry (if appropriate), the peak location(s) in terms of variable value (*x* axis) and any internal gaps, also in terms of the variable values.
➢ Continuing in context, provide the center position in terms of the ordered observations AND the approximate center value using the appropriate class interval values. Discuss the spread of distribution (minimum to maximum but excluding distinct outliers).
➢ Identify any outliers. Outliers are observations that are *clearly outside* the observed pattern. Look for values of the variable that are apart from most values on either end. Give both the number of outliers and their location in terms of the variable values. Remember context.

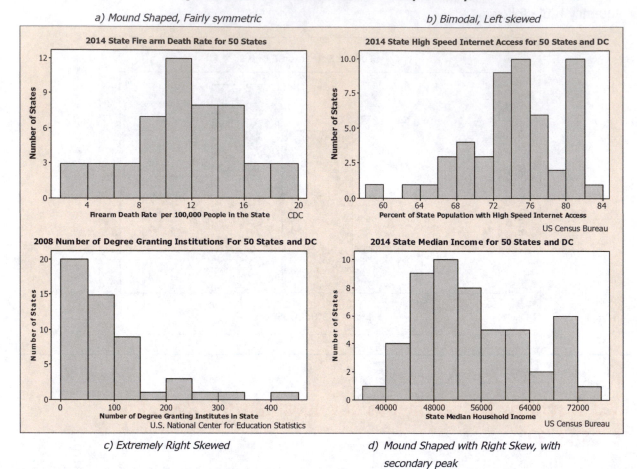

Quantitative Variable Distribution Shape Examples

a) Mound Shaped, Fairly symmetric

b) Bimodal, Left skewed

c) Extremely Right Skewed

d) Mound Shaped with Right Skew, with secondary peak

In determining the <u>shape of the distribution of a quantitative variable</u> from real data, you are looking for general tendencies. (The following are not contextual discussions of the entire behavior of the distribution; they are some guiding thoughts to help you with your shape determinations.)

a) **Symmetrical distributions** look similar on the left and right sides. Some are mound shaped like this one, others may look rectangular, and others may look like two side-by-side mounds, as seen in the next example. And these are just a few possibilities.

b) **Left-skewed distributions** have long "tails" on the left side but the concentration of observations is on the right side. This particular distribution is interesting in that there are two peaks (bimodal) on that right side.

c) **Right-skewed distributions** have long "tails" on the right side but the data are concentrated on the left. This distribution has most of its observations in the first two bars and then the frequency in each bar falls fairly dramatically. This distribution also happens to show an outlying observation to the far right.

QUANTITATIVE LITERACY AND REASONING

d) This **right-skewed distribution** has its observations concentrated on the right side, but they are more spread out among the bars, which results in a more "rounded" or mound shape. There is a definite tendency of the observations to be much fewer in frequency as the variable values get larger. This distribution also has a second, though less frequent, peak in values to the far right side.

Other things to look for in describing the distribution of a variable:

➢ **Internal gaps** are "empty bars" or gaps inside the histogram. Such a gap represents a class that has a zero frequency. Imagine the class between six and eight in the next histogram having no height . . . that would be an internal gap.

➢ **Outliers** are separated from the rest of the data; most of the data are close together but outliers are off by themselves. Small gaps, a single class for example, may not be enough to result in an outlier . . . part of the decision depends on the context.

➢ **Center** requires us to determine two things: **position** and **value**. To find center position, you need to know the number of observations, so sum the frequency of each of the classes/bars. That sum is n in the expression $\frac{n+1}{2}$. The result of this calculation provides position. If you have an even number of observations, the position will be between two observation-ordered observations and you report it as such. If you have an odd number of observations, the position will be on one of the ordered observations. To find the center value (actually values as you will report the interval of the appropriate class), you sum the class/bar frequencies that hold the center position–ordered observations.

➢ **Spread** is minimum to maximum but leaves out distinctive outliers.

➢ In looking for **peaks**, focus on distinctive upward movements (ask if a fairly large proportion of the observations is in the bar), little ups and downs are simply the nature of real data. Two distinctive peaks (bimodal) can indicate subgroups of individuals . . . grouping resulting from the influence of some second and perhaps unknown variable on the variable you are actually analyzing. Note two side-by-side high bars are a single peak, use the highest frequency bar's variable values to identify. It the two bars happen to have the same frequency, report the variable values from the beginning of the first of those bars to the end of the second.

EXAMPLE 3 AND YOUR TURN 1: All the real analysis work we do is contextual. But nearly all of us START with a few quick notes on or beside the graph BEFORE we start writing contextually. To illustrate that process, here are three histograms that have no context. Concentrate on the distribution characteristics only. Analyze the graph, identifying the indicated key pieces of information, and use this approach PRIOR to your contextual work, it will make the writing much easier! Just be sure you identify the key pieces of information! The first is done for you. It is in the cryptic note form used in my own prewrite. It also includes instructions for finding center! *This form is never acceptable for graded work! It is PREP work that saves time later!*

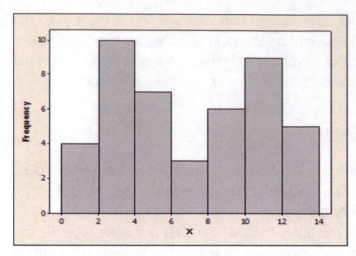

Two fairly symmetrical mounds.

Bimodal (2) with a primary peak between 2 and 4, secondary peak between 10 and 12.

Sum of frequencies, $n = 44$ total observations.

Center position: $\frac{n+1}{2} = \frac{45}{2} = 22.5$, so the center position is between the 22nd and 23rd ordered observations.

Summing from left to find those positions: Both the 22nd and 23rd observations are in the fourth bar. So, the center value is between 6 and 8.

Spread is from 0 to 14, no outliers or internal gaps.

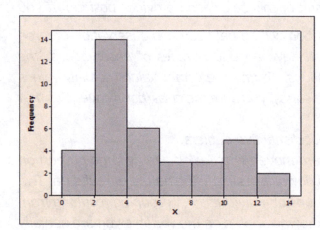

Shape:

Number of observations: _____

Center position calculation: _____

Center value: _____

Spread:_____

Other:

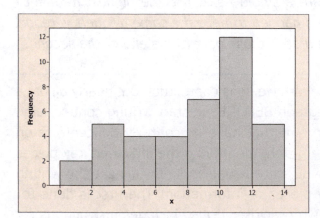

Shape:

Number of observations: _____

Center position calculation: _____

Center value: _____

Spread:_____

Other:

The next example applies these skills in writing contextual descriptive responses to a set of questions about the different variable distribution characteristics.

QUANTITATIVE LITERACY AND REASONING

EXAMPLE 4: The histogram below shows the distribution of the average live births per woman between 2010 and 2015 for 241 countries. The data are from UNdata, a service of the United Nations (http://data.un.org/).

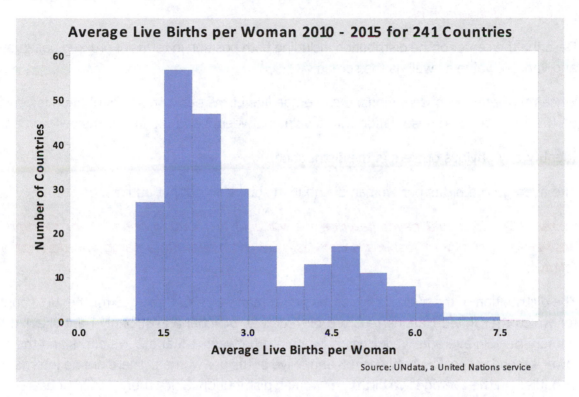

Respond to each of the following using self-contained sentences. Remember that context is critical!

***Be sure you describe the distribution of the variable NOT the histogram*!**

a) What is the variable? (Remember the variable is defined for one individual)?

The variable displayed is the average live births per woman from 2010 to 2015 for one of the countries reported by the United Nations.

b) Who/what are the individuals? Do these individuals represent a sample or a population?

The individuals are the 241 countries for which the United Nations reported birth data. Since there are more than 241 countries, the individuals represent a sample.

c) Using the information of **a** and **b** to clearly identify the distribution under discussion, describe the basic shape of the distribution along with variable values of peaks and any internal gaps.

The distribution of the average live births per woman from 2010 to 2015 for the 241 countries for which the United Nations reported birth data is bimodal and strongly right skewed. The primary peak in average live births per woman is between 1.5 and 2 live births and the much lower secondary peak is between 4.5 and 5 live births per woman. There are no internal gaps in the average live births per woman distribution.

Note how a and b are incorporated into this response; remember to put the variable description right after "distribution of."

d) Describe the center of the distribution including both position in terms of ordered observations and variable value as well as the spread.

Since there are 241 observations, the average live births per woman distribution is centered on the 121st ordered observation with a value between 2 and 2.5 live births per woman.

e) Identify any obvious outliers in the distribution.

The average live births per woman distribution shows no distinct outliers.

In real life, we would never describe the variable distribution behavior in question and answer form but these responses can easily be combined into a paragraph description as follows:

The distribution of the average live births per woman from 2010 to 2015 for the 241 countries for which the United Nations reported birth data is bimodal and strongly right skewed. The primary peak in average live births per woman is between 1.5 and 2 live births and the much lower secondary peak is between 4.5 and 5 live births per woman. There are no internal gaps or outliers in the average live births per woman distribution. Since there are 241 observations, the average live births per woman distribution is centered on the 121st ordered observation with a value between 2 and 2.5 live births per woman.

f) What does the distinctive shape of the distribution suggest? Discuss potential reasons for this shape.

- First consider, what IS the distinctive shape? Distinctive shapes often have important underlying causes. Once you see something distinctive . . . like two peaks or extreme outliers . . . you must then try to come up for reasons for what you see. Ask what might lead to this variable behavior?

- Then "brainstorm" possible causes! Only when you have some possibilities of what might cause what you are seeing do you have any chance of collecting and analyzing data to uncover the cause!

The distinctive bimodal shape suggests that there might be some other variable that separates the countries' average live births per woman into two "subgroups." When we looked at the scatterplot of this variable and the infant deaths per 1,000 live births in Chapter 3, it was clear that there was a tendency of the average live births per woman for a country to increase as

QUANTITATIVE LITERACY AND REASONING

the number of infant deaths per 1,000 live births in a country increased. It is likely that both of these variables respond to another variable or variables, most likely related to poverty and minimal access to health care.

This is the type of thinking process that you would use and communicate for this type of question. Each paragraph was a logical progression formed out of consideration of the idea(s) of the previous paragraph. This is a question about thinking critically to come up with POSSIBLE explanations for what you see and then communicating that logical progression to your reader in a way that says, "I have thought this through." You are not presenting evidence that what you are saying is factual but rather that you have considered it thoughtfully and, in enough detail, to make follow-up and gathering of additional information to seek out such evidence possible.

YOUR TURN 2: The histogram below shows the distribution of the six-year graduation rate for 52 US public universities which had 15,000 to 20,000 students in 2007. The data represent all such public institutions reported by The Education Trust. http://www.collegeresults.org/

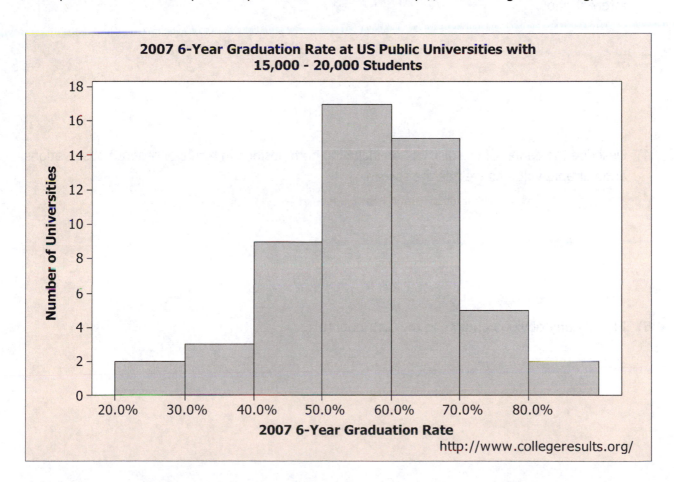

Respond to each of the following using self-contained sentences. Remember that context is critical!

1) What is the variable? (Remember the variable is defined for one individual)

2) Who/what are the individuals? Do these individuals represent a sample or a population?

3) Describe the basic shape of the distribution along with variable values of peaks and any internal gaps.

4) Describe the center of the distribution including both position in terms of ordered observations and variable value as well as the spread.

5) Identify any obvious outliers in the distribution.

QUANTITATIVE LITERACY AND REASONING

4.3 NUMBER SUMMARIES FOR QUANTITATIVE VARIABLES

Based on what is seen in the histogram, the analysis continues by producing the appropriate set of number summaries to summarize the variable's distribution numerically. Typically, we minimally need a measure of center and a measure of spread or variability around that center. In some cases, measures of position are also useful.

4.3.1 Measures of Center or Average

The three most common measures of center/average are the mean, median, and mode(s).

➤ The **mean** is what most of us grew up calling an average. It is found by summing all of the values and then dividing by the number of observations. Note that the formulas for the mean of population values and the mean of a sample values are the same, but the notation used to represent them is different. Population number summaries are represented by lower case Greek letters.

$$\bar{x} = \frac{\Sigma x}{n} \text{ for samples} \qquad \mu = \frac{\Sigma x}{N} \text{ for populations}$$

Means are especially sensitive to extreme values, so should not be used when the graphical analysis indicates extreme outliers or skew.

➤ The **median** is the center of the ordered values of the distribution. It is both a measure of position (location) and center. When, with our histograms, we found the center position in terms of ordered observations and then located the bar(s), we were estimating the median value. To find the median by hand:

- Put the values in order from smallest to largest

- Find the center position in the same way we did with the histogram: $\frac{n+1}{2}$

- If the result of the previous calculation is an integer, simply count your values until you reach that integer count, and the value in that position is the median.

- If the result of the calculation is 0.5, it indicates that the median is located between two of the values. So again, count until you reach the indicated integer count, then take the value in that position and the value in the position above it, add the two values and divide by two to get the median value.

The median is the preferable measure of center/average when the data have extreme outliers or skew, because the median is unaffected.

➤ The **mode** is the most frequently occurring value. Some data sets have no modes, some have multiple modes. In data sets with multiple modes, knowing those values can provide insights. But as a dependable measure of center, the mode is rarely the first-choice measure of center.

EXAMPLE 5: Find the mean, median, and mode for the following values from a sample.

| 93 | 71 | 86 | 86.5 | 68.5 | 80.5 | 72 | 67.5 | 83.5 | 94 | 92.5 | 75 |

a) Mean: $\bar{x} = \dfrac{\Sigma x}{n} = \dfrac{970}{12} = 80.8333$

b) Median: values are sorted and then numbered from 1 to 12

67.5	68.5	71	72	75	80.5	83.5	86	86.5	92.5	93	94
1	2	3	4	5	6	7	8	9	10	11	12

Find position: $\dfrac{n+1}{2} = \dfrac{12+1}{2} = \dfrac{13}{2} = 6.5$, so the median is between the sixth and seventh ordered observations.

Select the sixth and seventh values, sum and divide by two: $\dfrac{80.5+83.5}{2} = \dfrac{164}{2} = 82$ is the median value.

c) Mode: since there are no repeated values, there is no mode for this data set. ◼

YOUR TURN 3: Find the mean, median, and mode for the following values from a sample.

| 79.0 | 96.5 | 80.0 | 73.0 | 75.0 | 97.0 | 83.0 | 89.0 | 78.5 | 83.0 | 86.0 |

EXAMPLE 6: Determining the measure of center based on situation. Consider the following quantitative variables. Think about the expected shape tendencies of the distribution (left skewed, right skewed, symmetrical) or other relevant situational information. Which measure of center is the best choice? Justify your response.

a) Prices of homes in a certain geographic region

Although you will find low-price, medium-price, and high-price homes in most geographic areas, there are nearly always a few homes that are exceptionally luxurious with the prices to match. Those outliers would pull the mean too high. Use the median.

b) Length of parts coming off an assembly line that is functioning well

Though the lengths of all parts will not be exactly the same if precisely measured, an assembly line that is functioning well will produce parts that are very close to the length specified. The actual length of the measurements should fall randomly on either side of the specified value. Distribution of lengths is expected to be mound shaped and symmetrical. Use the mean.

c) Income of employees working in a chicken processing plant, where those on the line earn a set hourly wage

In this type of environment, there are many employees that earn the same or nearly the same income, then there are several "leads" that earn a somewhat higher income, followed by a few managers that may earn a true living wage and then there are three or four officers of the company which earn salaries that are very high. For most salary situation, medians are typically best choice due to the right-skewed shape. However, in the scenario just described, the mode "income" may actually represent a more accurate view of what most employees are making and attempting to live on.

YOUR TURN 4: Determining the measure of center based on situation. Consider the following quantitative variables. Based on variable's expected distribution shape, which measure of center is the best choice? Justify your response.

a) Salaries of team members on a professional football team

b) Heights of 20-year-old men

c) Grades on an easy exam

4.3.2 Measures of Position

Measures of position split data sets into groups of equal (or nearly equal) size. The most common measures of position are quartiles, which split the observations into four equal size groups.

➤ The first quartile has 25% of the data at or below it. Also, called the 25th percentile.
➤ The second quartile is the median and has 50% of the data at or below it. It is the 50th percentile.
➤ The third quartile has 75% of the data at or below it and is the 75th percentile.

These three quartiles combined with the minimum and maximum make up the five-number summary. The procedure for finding the quartiles is essentially the same as finding the median.

EXAMPLE 7: Find the positions and values of the five-number summary. Here are the sorted and numbered observations from Example 1.

67.5	68.5	71	72	75	80.5	83.5	86	86.5	92.5	93	94
1	2	3	4	5	6	7	8	9	10	11	12

Summary	Position	Value
Minimum	1	67.5
First quartile	Between third/fourth	71.5
Median	Between sixth/seventh	82
Third quartile	Between ninth/tenth	89.5
Maximum	12	94

The five-number summary must always be reported in this order.

Notice that the three quartiles split the data into groups of three observations.

Starting with sorted values, provide the position and value of the minimum and maximum.

Find median position: $\dfrac{12+1}{2} = 6.5$, median between sixth and seventh ordered observations.

Median value is $\dfrac{80.5+83.5}{2} = \dfrac{164}{2} = 82$

Next, find first quartile position (median of lower half of the data) $\dfrac{6+1}{2} = 3.5$, first quartile between third and fourth ordered observations.

First quartile value is $\dfrac{71+72}{2} = \dfrac{143}{2} = 71.5$

Finally, use the first quartile position information to find third quartile position. First quartile is between third and fourth ordered observations, count to third and fourth position in upper half of data. Using position 7 as count 1, count 3, and count 4 correspond to positions 9 and 10.

Third quartile value is $\dfrac{86.5+92.5}{2} = \dfrac{179}{2} = 89.5$

If these values represent student scores on an exam, how would you interpret the first quartile? The median?

Response: On this exam, about 25% of the students scored 71.5 points or lower. Fifty percent of the students scored an 82 or lower.

YOUR TURN 5: Find the positions and values of the five-number summary. This is the same data from Your Turn 3, so you can just copy that sorted data.

79.0	96.5	80.0	73.0	75.0	97.0	83.0	89.0	78.5	83.0	86.0

If these values represent course grades for several students, how would you interpret the third quartile?

Boxplots are graphical representations of the five-number summary.

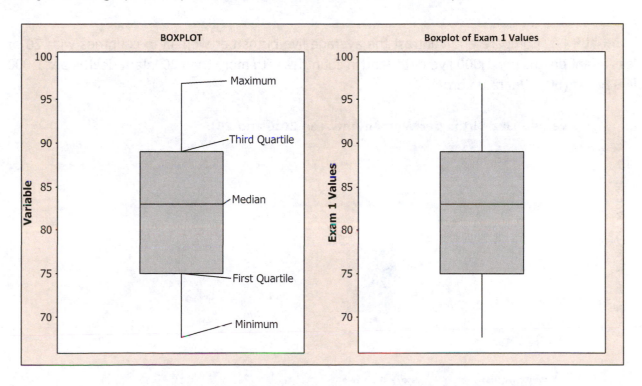

Boxplots do not replace distribution graphs like histogram, as they do not allow the identification of peaks and many gaps. One of the best use of boxplots is in getting a quick view of similarities and differences between related sets of data.

EXAMPLE 8: Use the boxplots to compare (how are they similar) and contrast (how are they different) student scores on exams 1 and 2.

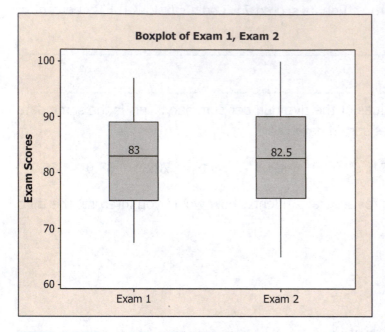

We can easily see that the exam score median values were very similar, with about half of the students scoring 82/83 or above on both exams. It also appears that on both exams, about 25% made 89/90 and above and that about 75% made around 75% and above. The middle 50% of scores (seen in the dark rectangles) were very similar on both exams.

However, the minimum score on exam 2 is lower than the minimum on exam 1. The maximum score on exam 2 is higher than the maximum score on exam 1.

YOUR TURN 6: Compare and contrast the average live births per woman in countries with 20 or less infant deaths per 1,000 live births and in countries with more than 20 infant deaths per 1,000 live births (http://data.un.org/).

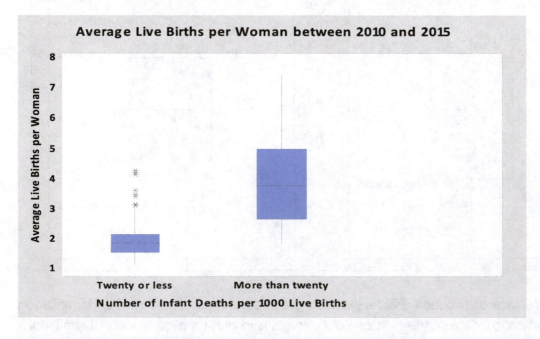

The asterisks * on the 20 or less boxplot indicate outliers.

QUANTITATIVE LITERACY AND REASONING

4.3.3 Measures of Spread or Variability

Once we have determined the appropriate center measure, we must now include the corresponding measure of spread.

If the variable distribution was symmetric with no extreme outliers, then the mean was the appropriate measure of center. The standard deviation is the number summary that gives spread around the mean.

$$s = \sqrt{\frac{\Sigma(x - \bar{x})^2}{n - 1}} \text{ for samples} \qquad \sigma = \sqrt{\frac{\Sigma(x - \mu)^2}{N}} \text{ for populations}$$

If the variable distribution was skewed or showed clear outliers, then the median was the appropriate measure of center. We use the interquartile range (IQR) to look at spread around the median.

$$IQR = Q3 - Q1$$

The IQR is the difference between the third and first quartiles. It indicates the range of the middle 50% values (the rectangle seen in the boxplot).

EXAMPLE 9: Once again we look at the data used in Example 1. Find the standard deviation and IQR.

93	71	86	86.5	68.5	80.5	72	67.5	83.5	94	92.5	75

x	$x - \bar{x}$	$(x - \bar{x})^2$
93	12.16667	148.027778
71	−9.83333	96.6944444
86	5.166667	26.6944444
86.5	5.666667	32.1111111
68.5	−12.3333	152.111111
80.5	−0.33333	0.11111111
72	−8.83333	78.0277778
67.5	−13.3333	177.777778
83.5	2.666667	7.11111111
94	13.16667	173.361111
92.5	11.66667	136.111111
75	−5.83333	34.0277778
		1062.16667

Inserting highlighted sum from table:

$$s = \sqrt{\frac{\Sigma(x - \bar{x})^2}{n - 1}} = \sqrt{\frac{1062.16667}{12 - 1}} \approx 9.8265$$

Using the first and third quartiles from Example 3:

$$IQR = Q3 - Q1 = 89.5 - 71.5 = 18$$

YOUR TURN 7: Once again we look at the data from Your Turn 3. Find the standard deviation and IQR.

79.0	96.5	80.0	73.0	75.0	97.0	83.0	89.0	78.5	83.0	86.0

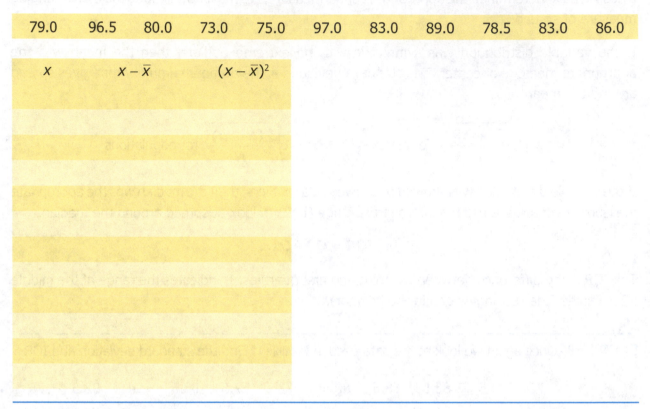

x	$x - \bar{x}$	$(x - \bar{x})^2$

EXAMPLE 10: Looking again at the distribution of the average live births per woman between 2010 and 2015 for 241 countries, seen earlier in the chapter, which set of number summaries would you suggest? Explain your answer (http://data.un.org/).

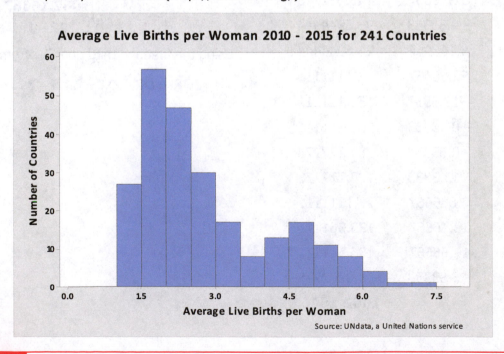

Average Live Births per Woman 2010 - 2015 for 241 Countries

Source: UNdata, a United Nations service

QUANTITATIVE LITERACY AND REASONING

Because the distribution of the of the average live births per woman between 2010 and 2015 for 241 countries was strongly right skewed, we must use the median along with the rest of the five-number summary. The quartiles would not be pulled too high by the right skew like the mean.

Given the distinctive characteristics of the distribution, would a single set of number summaries really "characterize" the variable's behavior? Explain.

Given the distinctive bimodal shape a single set of number summaries really would not provide a great deal of information to characterize the behavior of the variable. Since the two peaks suggests the potential for underlying subgroups, it would be better to also include number summaries for both subgroups, if possible, in addition to the summaries for the entire data set.

YOUR TURN 8: Based on the shape of the distribution for the six-year graduation rate, which set of number summaries would you suggest we use? (mean and standard deviation OR five-number summary) Explain your answer. The data were reported by The Education Trust. http://www.collegeresults.org/.

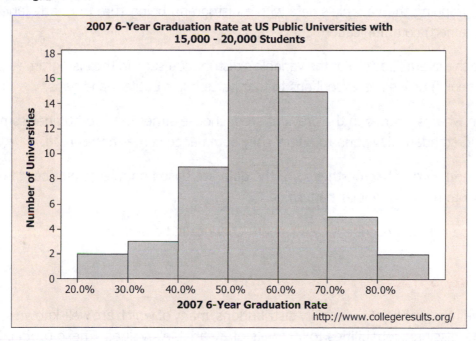

Shape and measures of center insights: Although there are certainly exceptions to the following guidelines, there are some general tendencies in the behavior of the mean and median with respect to shape. In clearly symmetrical distributions, we expect medians and means that are close in value. In distributions that are clearly left skewed, typically the mean is pulled lower in value by the long left tail, resulting in mean values less than median values. Right-skewed distributions have long right tails that tend to pull the mean higher, so typically mean values are greater than median values. So, not only does seeing the shape provide insight into how the mean and median will likely be related, knowing the mean and median values can provide insight into the potential shape of the distribution with respect to skew direction or symmetry.

4.4 INTRODUCTION TO DENSITY CURVES AND NORMAL DISTRIBUTIONS

So far in this chapter, we discussed two types of tools for describing the distribution of a quantitative variable, graphical, and numerical, and we have a general strategy for exploring a quantitative variable:

1) Start by graphing the variable's data with a histogram, being sure to clearly label it for good (self-contained) communication!

2) Describe the overall pattern of the variable's distribution seen in the histogram (shape, center, spread, peaks) as well as exceptions to that pattern like outliers and gaps.

3) Based on what is learned in the previous step, choose either the five-number summary or the mean and standard deviation to numerically summarize center and spread.

   We now add a potential fourth step. If the data are based on a large number of observations and seem to follow a regular pattern:

4) We may be able to describe it by a smooth curve called a density curve.

4.4.1 Density Curves

Density curves are graphs of probability distributions, many of which are well-known mathematical functions that assign probabilities to intervals of a variable's values. These probabilities, which represent the likelihood that a value in a defined interval will occur, are found by determining the area under the density curve. *A density curve has a total area of 1 and is entirely at or above the horizontal axis*. Four of an infinite number of density curves are seen in the graphic below. (Note the familiar distribution shapes. Starting at the upper left: right skewed, left skewed, and from the bottom left: symmetrical and rectangular, symmetrical, and mound or bell shaped.)

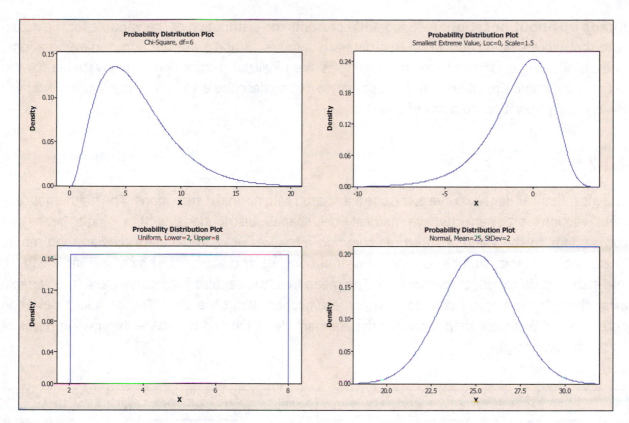

Probabilities are always values between 0 and 1. A probability of 1 means the outcome is guaranteed. A probability of 0 means the outcome can never occur. All other probabilities are represented in fraction or decimal form.

The basic idea that takes us from histogram to density curve is as follows: Draw a curve through the center of each bar in a histogram, smoothing out the irregular ups and downs of the bars. Though we have worked primarily with histograms where the heights of the bars represented the number of individuals in each class, those heights could also be expressed as a proportion or percentage of individuals in each class. If the pattern observed is one that fits a common density curve, then we can use areas under that density curve to assign probabilities of outcomes within intervals of the value. The basic process is illustrated graphically below.

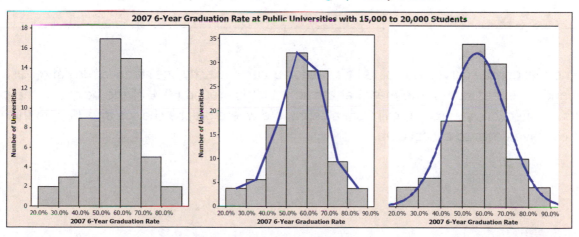

Heads up about notation: A histogram represents the distribution of the variable for the actual data that were studied and when that data are samples, $\bar{x}$ and s are the appropriate notations. The density curve, on the other hand, reflects the idealized distribution of the variable for the entire population. So, when you use a density curve to describe a variable's distribution, you will always use population notation of μ and σ.

4.4.2 Normal Distributions

The most familiar density curve is the one associated with normal distributions. The mathematically ideal versions are perfectly symmetrical, bell-shaped distributions with a single peak that corresponds to the value of the three common measures of center: mean, median, and mode. There are an infinite number of normal distributions, each characterized by a specific mean, μ, and standard deviation, σ combination. The mean fixes the center of the curve along the variable axis; changing the mean changes the curve's location along the axis. The standard deviation determines the curve's shape; change the standard deviation and the shape changes in terms of its spread and height.

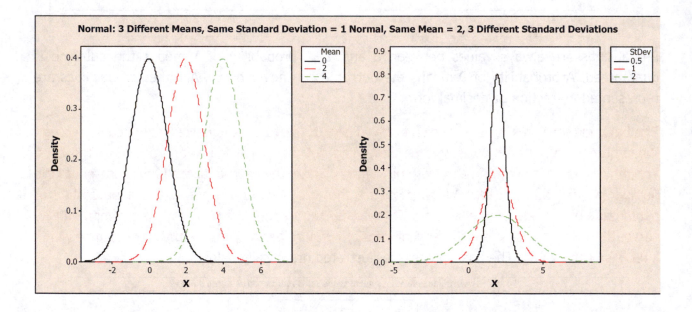

On a normal density curve, the points of inflection occur at exactly one standard deviation distance from and on either side of the mean, at a height that is around 60% of the height of the peak. Points of inflection, you may recall from algebra, are where graphs change direction, in this case from concave down to concave up.

QUANTITATIVE LITERACY AND REASONING

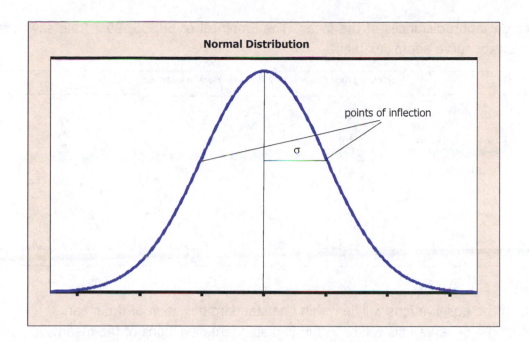

Normal Distribution

points of inflection

σ

Caution is advised before jumping to the conclusion that a variable is normally distributed just because it looks bell shaped on a graph! There are several different families of density curves that are symmetric and bell shaped but are NOT normally distributed (and thus would assign different probabilities to the intervals.

Also, keep in mind that no real-world data match any of the idealized curves exactly, so the fit is not expected to be perfect when we go from real data to an "ideal model." Though what we observe in a graphical approach, like shown with the graduation rate data earlier, can give us an indication of a potential fit, visual examination is not sufficient to decide that the variable is normally distributed. Statistical techniques beyond the scope of this book can give far more definitive evidence. You will always be told in this book when the variable has been determined to be approximately normal.

Empirical Rule (68, 95, 99.7 Rule)

Though there are an infinite number of normal distributions, the relationship between mean, standard deviation, and points of inflection make the standard deviation the perfect and natural "unit of measurement" for normal distributions. The area beneath the curve for all normal curves, for any mean and standard deviation combination, remains constant when that area is for the same distances measured in terms of the *number of standard deviations* from the mean. This fact leads us to our first rule for approximating the percentages of observations that lie within certain standard deviation distances of the mean. The Empirical or 68, 95, 99.7 Rule says that in any normal density curve approximately:

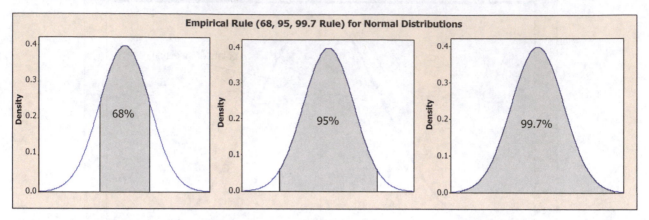

Empirical Rule (68, 95, 99.7 Rule) for Normal Distributions

➤ 68% of the observations will lie within one standard deviation of the mean.
➤ 95% of the observations will lie within two standard deviations of the mean.
➤ 99.7% of the observations will lie within three standard deviations of the mean.

To the right, note the "zoomed" view of the tail of the 99.7% graph.

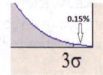

99.7% is not 100%. There is a small but relevant area beyond the three standard deviations on both sides. 100% − 99.7% = 0.3%

That 0.3% is split equally between the two tails, for 0.15% per tail.

EXAMPLE 11: The distribution of SAT Critical Reading scores for 2015 college-bound high school seniors were standardized so that they are approximately normally distributed with a mean of 495 and a standard deviation of 116. Use the 68-95-99.7 rule to answer the questions that follow. Remember to label and describe the variable.

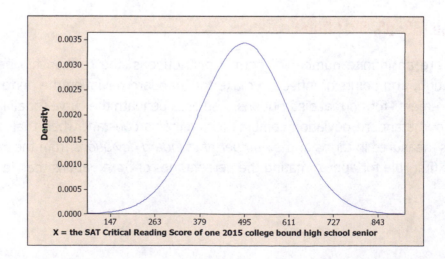

X = the SAT Critical Reading Score of one 2015 college bound high school senior

a) Approximately what percentage of college-bound high school seniors had SAT Critical Reading scores less than 147? **According to the rule, 0.15% of observations are three standard deviations below the mean.**

Since SAT Critical Reading scores for 2015 college-bound high school seniors were standardized so that they are approximately normally distributed with a mean of 495 and a standard deviation of 116, approximately 0.15% of these college-bound high school seniors had SAT Critical Reading scores less than 147.

b) Approximately what percentage of college-bound high school seniors had SAT Critical Reading scores above 379? **The area from 379 to 495 is half of the middle 68% interval, thus 34%. Since 100% of the area is under the entire curve, 50% is above 495. 34% + 50% = 84%**

Since SAT Critical Reading scores for 2015 college-bound high school seniors were standardized so that they are approximately normally distributed with a mean of 495 and a standard deviation of 116, approximately 84% of these college-bound high school seniors had SAT Critical Reading scores above 379.

c) Approximately what percentage of college-bound high school seniors had SAT Critical Reading scores between 379 and 727? **We know the area from 379 to 495 is 34%. The area from 495 to 727 is half of the 95% interval or 47.5%. 34% + 47.5% = 81.5%**

Since SAT Critical Reading scores for 2015 college-bound high school seniors were standardized so that they are approximately normally distributed with a mean of 495 and a standard deviation of 116, approximately 81.5% of these college-bound high school seniors had SAT Critical Reading scores between 379 and 727.

YOUR TURN 9: The distribution of SAT Critical Reading scores for 2015 college-bound high school seniors were standardized so that they are approximately normally distributed with a mean of 495 and a standard deviation of 116. Use the 68-95-99.7 rule to answer the questions that follow. Remember the variable label and description as well as the self-contained sentence responses.

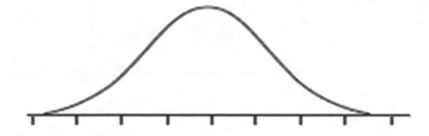

X =

a) Approximately what percentage of college-bound high school seniors had SAT Critical Reading scores less than 263?

b) Approximately what percentage of college-bound high school seniors had SAT Critical Reading scores above 147?

c) Approximately what percentage of college-bound high school seniors had SAT Critical Reading scores between 263 and 843? The College Board reports a maximum score of 800 on their standardized scale.

Z-scores and the Standard Normal Table

As good as the empirical rule is for quick and dirty estimates of the percentage of outcomes within certain intervals, those estimates only work for exactly one, two, or three standard deviations. Typically, however, we need better estimates and estimates for other standard deviation distances from the mean. Our answer is to use z-scores and the standard normal table.

Recall the earlier discussion about the relationship between mean, standard deviation, and points of inflection in normal distributions. That relationship makes *the standard deviation the perfect and natural "unit of measurement"* for normal distributions. The area beneath the curve for all normal curves, with any mean, standard deviation combination, remains constant when that area is based on the same distances from the mean in terms of the *number of standard deviations*. In addition to enabling the use of the empirical rule, these normal distribution characteristics also mean we can transform or standardize any normal distribution into the Standard Normal Distribution. This is very handy, because estimating areas under the normal curve for any interval of values mathematically requires some pretty sophisticated calculus. But by standardizing, we can use a single table to find fairly accurate probabilities for normal curves with any mean and standard deviation.

The Standard Normal distribution has $\mu = 0$ and $\sigma = 1$. Its scale is measured in number of standard deviation units. The standard score or z-score formula is: $z = \dfrac{x - \mu}{\sigma}$. When we input a value of x, along with the original distributions μ and σ, the resulting value of z indicates the distance that x was from the original μ in standard deviations units. Negative z-scores indicate values below the mean, positive z-scores are above the mean.

Begin by pulling out the standard normal table located in Appendix II in the back of the book. Notice that there are two pages, one for negative z values and one for positive z value. The table gives probabilities **below** a specified z-score. Our z-scores are always rounded to two decimal places; the probabilities have four decimal places.

EXAMPLE 12: Standard Normal Table Use

z	.00	.01	.02	.03	.04	.05	.0
−3.8	.0001	.0001	.0001	.0001	.0001	.0001	.00(
−3.7	.0001	.0001	.0001	.0001	.0001	.0001	.00(
−3.6	.0002	.0002	.0001	.0001	.0001	.0001	.00(
−3.5	.0002	.0002	.0002	.0002	.0002	.0002	.00(
−3.4	.0003	.0003	.0003	.0003	.0003	.0003	.00(
−3.3	.0005	.0005	.0005	.0004	.0004	.0004	.00(

To find the probability below a $z = -3.53$, you look down the left side (labelled z) to the row labelled −3.5, then look for the column labelled for .03, where the −3.5 row intersects the .03 column is the probability of a z value less than −3.53. $P(z < -3.53) = 0.0002$

z	.00	.01	.02	.03
0.0	.5000	.5040	.5080	.5120
0.1	.5398	.5438	.5478	.5517
0.2	.5793	.5832	.5871	.5910
0.3	.6179	.6217	.6255	.6293
0.4	.6554	.6591	.6628	.6664
0.5	.6915	.6950	.6985	.7019
0.6	.7257	.7291	.7324	.7357
0.7	.7580	.7611	.7642	.7673
0.8	.7881	.7910	.7939	.7967
0.9	.8159	.8186	.8212	.8238
1.0	.8413	.8438	.8461	.8485

To find the probability below a $z = 1.02$, look down the left (labelled z) to 1, then read across the top to find .02. Find the intersection. $P(z < 1.02) = 0.8461$

To find the probability greater than 1.02, we must turn the problem into a less than problem as follows:

$$P(z > 1.02) = 1 - P(z < 1.02)$$
$$= 1 - 0.8461 = 0.1539$$

To find the probability between −3.53 and 1.02, we must find the probability of the larger z value and subtract the probability of the smaller z value as follows:

$P(-3.53 < z < 1.02)$ is the quantity we need. We must turn this into two "less than" statements. The one with the largest probability MUST go first, so though it seems odd, these are the math steps:

$$P(-3.53 < z < 1.02) = P(z < 1.02) - P(z < -3.53) = .8461 - .0002 = 0.8459$$

In completing standard normal table-type problems, you are expected to show all the mathematical steps, including notation, as shown in the examples that follow.

EXAMPLE 13: The distribution of SAT Critical Reading scores for 2015 college-bound high school seniors are standardized so that they are approximately normally distributed with a mean of 495 and a standard deviation of 116. **Use the standard normal table to answer the questions that follow**. Show ALL appropriate mathematics steps, notations, and interpret the results in context.

What is the probability that a senior randomly selected from the 2015 college-bound high school seniors that took the SAT had a Critical Reading score of no more than 400?

a) Sketch the distribution, labeling the variable and shading the area associated the indicated probability.

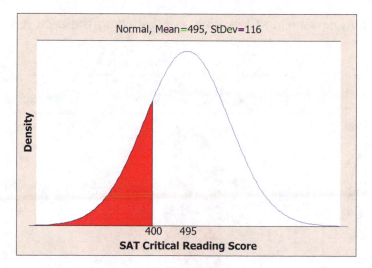

Normal, Mean=495, StDev=116

Density

400   495

SAT Critical Reading Score

b) Complete the mathematical steps using appropriate notation: Note that this problem requires us to standardize!

$$P(x < 400) = P\left(z < \frac{400 - 495}{116}\right)$$

$$= P(z < -.82) = 0.2061$$

c) Write a self-contained response to the question. Then respond to: Is outcome typical or unusual?

Since the distribution of SAT Critical Reading scores for 2015 college-bound high school seniors are standardized so that they are approximately normally distributed with a mean of 495 and a standard deviation of 116, the probability that a senior randomly selected from this group had a Critical Reading score of no more than 400 is 0.2061.

Since scores of less than 400 occur over one-fifth of the time, by chance alone, a score of less than 400 is quite typical.

EXAMPLE 14: The distribution of SAT Critical Reading scores for 2015 college-bound high school seniors are standardized so that they are approximately normally distributed with a mean of 495 and a standard deviation of 116. **Use the standard normal table to answer the questions that follow.** Show ALL appropriate mathematics steps, notations, and interpret the results in context.

What is the percentage of the 2015 college-bound high school seniors that took the SAT had a Critical Reading scores between 400 and 550?

a) Sketch the distribution, labeling the variable and shading the area associated the indicated probability.

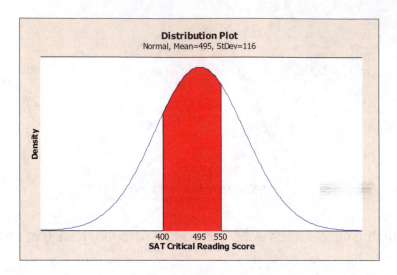

b) Complete the mathematical steps using appropriate notation: Note that this problem requires us to standardize!

$$P(400 < x < 550) = P(x < 550) - (x < 400) =$$

$$P\left(z < \frac{550 - 495}{116}\right) - P\left(z < \frac{400 - 495}{116}\right):$$

$$P(z < .47) - P(z < -.82) =$$

$$.6808 - .2061 = 0.4747$$

c) Write a self-contained response to the question. Then respond to: Is outcome typical or unusual?

Since the distribution of SAT Critical Reading scores for 2015 college-bound high school seniors are standardized so that they are approximately normally distributed with a mean of 495 and a standard deviation of 116, the percentage of these seniors that had a Critical Reading scores between 400 and 550 is about 47.47%.

Since scores between 400 and 550 occur almost half of the time, by chance alone, a score between 400 and 550 are very typical.

EXAMPLE 15: The distribution of SAT Critical Reading scores for 2015 college-bound high school seniors are standardized so that they are approximately normally distributed with a mean of 495 and a standard deviation of 116. **Use the standard normal table to answer the questions that follow**. Show ALL appropriate mathematics steps, notations, and interpret the results in context.

What proportion of the 2015 college-bound high school seniors that took the SAT had a Critical Reading score of at least 650?

a) Sketch the distribution, labeling the variable and shading the area associated the indicated probability.

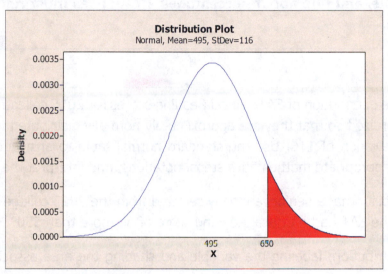

b) Complete the mathematical steps using appropriate notation: Note that this problem requires us to standardize!

$$P(x > 650) = 1 - P(x < 650)$$

$$1 - P\left(z < \frac{650 - 495}{116}\right) =$$

$$1 - P(z < 1.34) =$$

$$1 - .9099 = 0.0901$$

c) Write a self-contained response to the question. Then respond to: Is outcome typical or unusual?

Since the distribution of SAT Critical Reading scores for 2015 college-bound high school seniors are standardized so that they are approximately normally distributed with a mean of 495 and a standard deviation of 116, the proportion of these seniors that had a Critical Reading scores of 650 or more is about 0.0901.

Nearly 1 in every 11 students scored above 650, so scores above 650 are not unusual (though are certainly not common).

None of the three examples had outcomes that would be deemed unusual. None of the outcomes had probabilities that would rarely occur by chance. In 2015, 1.7 million college-bound high school students took the SAT. That means over 163,000 of them had Critical Reading scores at or above 650. Unusual results are those that are surprising when they occur . . . certainly occurring less than 1 in 20 times. Once the chance occurrence falls below 1 in 100 times, we begin to ask "what is going on?"

In the Your Turn problems that follow, notice that one question is about probability, one about proportions, and one about percentages. Responses must reflect the different questions asked.

YOUR TURN 10: The distribution of SAT Critical Reading scores for 2015 college-bound high school seniors are standardized so that they are approximately normally distributed with a mean of 495 and a standard deviation of 116. Use the standard normal table to answer the questions that follow. Show ALL appropriate mathematics steps, notations, and interpret the results in context.

What is the probability that a senior randomly selected from the 2015 college-bound high school seniors that took the SAT had a Critical Reading score of no more than 550?

a) Sketch the distribution, labeling the variable and shading the area associated the indicated probability.

b) Complete the mathematical steps using appropriate notation: Note that this problem requires us to standardize!

c) Write a self-contained response to the question. Then respond to: Is outcome typical or unusual?

YOUR TURN 11: The distribution of SAT Critical Reading scores for 2015 college-bound high school seniors are standardized so that they are approximately normally distributed with a mean of 495 and a standard deviation of 116. Use the standard normal table to answer the questions that follow. Show ALL appropriate mathematics steps, notations, and interpret the results in context.

What proportion of the 2015 college-bound high school seniors that took the SAT had a Critical Reading score of at least 550?

a) Sketch the distribution, labeling the variable and shading the area associated the indicated probability.

b) Complete the mathematical steps using appropriate notation: Note that this problem requires us to standardize!

c) Write a self-contained response to the question. Then respond to: Is outcome typical or unusual?

YOUR TURN 12: The distribution of SAT Critical Reading scores for 2015 college-bound high school seniors are standardized so that they are approximately normally distributed with a mean of 495 and a standard deviation of 116. Use the standard normal table to answer the questions that follow. Show ALL appropriate mathematics steps, notations, and interpret the results in context.

What percentage of the 2015 college-bound high school seniors that took the SAT had a Critical Reading score between 450 and 650?

a) Sketch the distribution, labeling the variable and shading the area associated the indicated probability.

b) Complete the mathematical steps using appropriate notation: Note that this problem requires us to standardize!

c) Write a self-contained response to the question. Then respond to: Is outcome typical or unusual?

YOUR TURN FINAL ANSWERS

Section 4.2

1) The second histogram is strongly right skewed with one peak between two and four. It has 37 observations, so the center position is on the 19th ordered observation. Summing the frequencies from the left, the 19th ordered observation is in the third bar, so the center value is between four and six. The spread is from 0 to 14. There are no outliers or internal gaps.

   The third histogram is strongly left skewed with one peak between 10 and 12. It has 39 observations, so the center position is on the 20th ordered observation, which falls in the fifth bar. The center value is between 8 and 10. The spread is from 0 to 14. There are no outliers or internal gaps.

2) a) The variable displayed is the 2007 six-year graduation rate of a US public university with 15,000 to 20,000 students.
   b) The individuals are 52 US public universities with 15,000 and 20,000 students in 2007 that were presented by The Education Trust. We have no way of knowing if the data presented by The Education Trust are for all US public universities of this size or only some of them. Thus, we must assume that the data represent a sample.
   c) The distribution of the 2007 six-year graduation rate of 52 US public universities with 15,000 to 20,000 students is mound shaped and symmetrical. These six-year graduation rates peak between 50% and 60%. There are no internal gaps in the graduation rates.
   d) Since there are 52 observations, the six-year graduation rates are centered between the 26th and 27th ordered observations with a value between 50% and 60%. The six-year graduation rates spread from 20% to 90%.
   e) The six-year graduation rate distribution shows no outlying universities.

Section 4.3

3) Mean: $\bar{x} \approx 83.6364$, median position: sixth ordered observation, median value = 83, mode = 83.

4) a) Median due to expected strong right-skewed distribution.
   b) Mean due to expected symmetrical distribution.
   c) Median due to expected left-skewed distribution.

5) ___73___   ___78.5___   ___83___   ___89___   ___97___

       1st   3rd   6th   9th   11th

   About 75% of the students had course grades of 89 or lower.

6) As mentioned in the distribution discussion in Example 2 of this chapter and in the scatterplot example in Chapter 3, the average live births per woman in the studied countries increased as

YOUR TURN FINAL ANSWERS

the number of infant deaths per 1,000 live births increased. The countries have been grouped into those countries where the number of infant deaths per 1,000 live births is 20 or less and those countries where the number of infant deaths per 1,000 live births is above 20.

Well, over half of the 241 studied countries fall into the 20 or less group and nearly all of them have three or less average live births per woman. The middle 50% of the countries in this group have average live births per woman between 1.5 and just above 2. Eight countries show up as outliers for this group with average births per woman up to 4.5. These outliers are the only significant overlap between the two infant mortality groups.

In those countries where the number of infant deaths per 1,000 live births is above 20, we can easily see that nearly all these countries have average live births per woman above the 1.8 live births which is the median for the 20 or less group. The middle 50% of the countries in this group have average live births per woman between 2.5 and 5. Almost 50% of the countries in the higher infant mortality group have average live births per woman of four or more, with a maximum of about 7.5 births.

7) $s \approx 7.9249$, IQR = 10.5

x	$(x - \bar{x})^2$	$(x - \bar{x})^2$
79	−4.63636	21.495868
96.5	12.86364	165.47314
80	−3.63636	13.22314
73	−10.6364	113.13223
75	−8.63636	74.586777
97	13.36364	178.58678
83	−0.63636	0.4049587
89	5.363636	28.768595
78.5	−5.13636	26.382231
83	−0.63636	0.4049587
86	2.363636	5.5867769
		622.45868

8) Because the distribution of six-year graduation rates is symmetrical and has no outliers, using the mean and standard deviation is the appropriate set of number summaries.

Section 4.4

9) Same variable label and scale as Example 1.

a) According to the rule, 2.5% of observations are two standard deviations below the mean. Since SAT Critical Reading scores for 2015 college-bound high school seniors were standardized so that they are approximately normally distributed with a mean of 495 and a standard deviation of 116, approximately 2.5% of these college-bound high school seniors had SAT Critical Reading scores less than 263.

b) The area from 147 to 495 is half of the middle 99.7% interval, thus 49.85%. Since 100% of the area is under the entire curve, 50% is above 495. 49.85% + 50% = 99.85%. Since SAT Critical Reading scores for 2015 college-bound high school seniors were standardized so that they are approximately normally distributed with a mean of 495 and a standard deviation of 116, approximately 99.85% of these college-bound high school seniors had SAT Critical Reading scores above 147.

c) The area from 263 to 495 is half of the middle 95%, thus 47.5%. The area from 495 to 843 is half of the 99.7% interval or 49.85%. 47.5% + 49.85% = 97.35%. Since SAT Critical Reading scores for 2015 college-bound high school seniors were standardized so that they are approximately normally distributed with a mean of 495 and a standard deviation of 116, approximately 97.25% of these college-bound high school seniors had SAT Critical Reading scores between 263 and 843. (But College Board reports a maximum of 800.)

10) a)

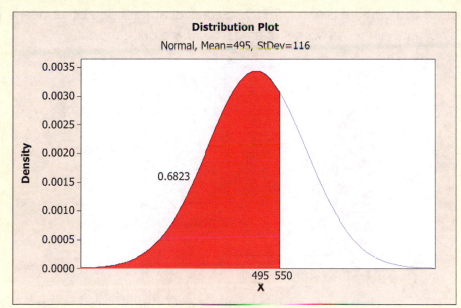

b) $P(x < 550) = P\left(z < \dfrac{550 - 495}{116}\right) = P(z < .47) = 0.6808$

c) Since the distribution of SAT Critical Reading scores for 2015 college-bound high school seniors are standardized so that they are approximately normally distributed with a mean of 495 and a standard deviation of 116, the probability that a senior randomly selected from this group had a Critical Reading score of no more than 550 is 0.6908. Scores at and below 550 almost 70% of the time, by chance alone, so scores of no more than 550 is very typical.

YOUR TURN FINAL ANSWERS

11) a)

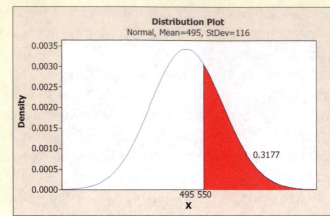

b) $P(x > 550) = 1 - P(x < 550) = 1 - P\left(z < \dfrac{550 - 495}{116}\right) = 1 - P(z < .47) = 1 - .6808 = 0.3192$

c) Since the distribution of SAT Critical Reading scores for 2015 college-bound high school seniors are standardized so that they are approximately normally distributed with a mean of 495 and a standard deviation of 116, the proportion of these seniors that had a Critical Reading scores of 550 or more is about 0.3192. Scores of at least 550 occur nearly a third of the time, by chance alone, so scores of at least 550 are quite typical.

12) a)

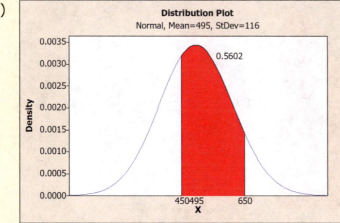

b) $P(450 < x < 650) = P(x < 650) - (x < 450) = P\left(z < \dfrac{650 - 495}{116}\right) - P\left(z < \dfrac{450 - 495}{116}\right) =$

$P(z < 1.34) - P(z < -.39) = .9099 - .3483 = 0.5616$

c) Since the distribution of SAT Critical Reading scores for 2015 college-bound high school seniors are standardized so that they are approximately normally distributed with a mean of 495 and a standard deviation of 116, the percentage of these seniors that had a Critical Reading scores between 450 and 650 is about 56.16%. Scores between 450 and 650 more than half of the time, by chance alone, so a score between 450 and 650 is very typical.

CHECK YOUR MASTERY

➢ **Chapter Terminology**: *If you do not know the meaning, record it here.*

Variable

Individual

Distribution

Quantitative Variable

Qualitative Variable

Pie Chart

Bar Chart

Frequency Distribution

Center (Value and Position)

Spread

Peak

Mode

Mean

Median

Five-Number Summary

Quartile

Position

Standard Deviation

Interquartile Range

Range

Sample

Population

Symmetrical

CHECK YOUR MASTERY

Left Skew

Right Skew

Outlier

Density Curve

Empirical Rule

Normal Distribution

Standard Normal Distribution

Z-Score (Standard Score)

Probability

Proportion

Percentage

➢ **Do you know**

- The normal distribution problem interpretation language?

- The *z*-score formula

- The notation for the mean and standard deviation for both sample and population?

➢ **Can you**

- Determine the individual and variable from a description?

- Determine when to use a bar chart, pie chart, or histogram?

- Completely describe the distribution of a quantitative variable, in context, based only on its histogram when the questions are provided?

- Determine (and explain) the appropriate set of number summaries based on the histogram?

- Find the positions in term of ordered observations of the five-number summary?

- Interpret the quartile values in context?

- Find the mean, standard deviation, and five-number summary values manually and with your calculator? (calculators do not give positions)

- Determine approximate percentages of observations in intervals of variable values based on the empirical rule?

- Complete all steps in the normal probability calculations based on the standard normal table using all appropriate notation (less than, greater than, and between probabilities)?

- Write complete contextual normal problem interpretations in proportion, probability, and percentage forms?

- Determine (and explain) whether a result is typical or unusual based on the normal probabilities?

Name_____ Section_____ date_____

EXERCISES

1) Use the relative frequency table shown below to respond to the items that follow.

US Educational Attainment of Age Percent of Age 25 Years and Over Population 2014	
No high school diploma	11.8
GED	3.1
High school diploma	26.7
Some college, no degree	16.6
Associate's degree	9.9
Bachelor's degree	14.9
Some graduate school, no degree	5.3
Master's degree	8.6
Professional degree	1.5
Doctorate degree	1.8

Sum > 100% due to rounding

Source: U.S. Census Bureau, Current Population Survey, 2014 Annual Social and Economic Supplement.

a) What is the variable? What are the values of the variable? (Recall that qualitative variable "values" are not typically numerical.)

b) What are the individuals?

c) Among the additional information that was reported with the information in this table was the total number of people represented, reported as 209,287 (in thousands). Represent the value in ordinary form without the "in thousands."

d) Could this data be represented in a pie chart? Explain.

e) Sketch a bar chart to represent the table's information. Be sure to include sufficient labeling for the reader to fully understand the graph with no additional information.

2) The table below was first published on the Bureau of Labor Statistics website in January 2015. This table is NOT a traditional frequency table. Instead, it reports quantitative variable information for combinations of qualitative variables' values. This is a very common format for published census information from the US government.

Median usual weekly earnings of full-time wage and salary workers age 25 and older by educational attainment, 2014 annual averages

Education level	Total	Men	Women	White	Black or African American	Asian	Hispanic or Latino
Total, all education levels	$839	$922	$752	$864	$674	$991	$619
Less than a high school diploma	488	517	409	493	440	477	466
High school graduates, no college	668	751	578	696	579	604	595
Some college or associate degree	761	872	661	791	637	748	689
Bachelor's degree only	1,101	1,249	965	1,132	895	1,149	937
Bachelor's degree and higher	1,193	1,385	1,049	1,219	970	1,328	1,007
Advanced degree	1,386	1,630	1,185	1,390	1,149	1,562	1,235

Bureau of Labor Statistics, U.S. Department of Labor. "Median Weekly Earnings by Educational Attainment in 2014." The Economics Daily. http://www.bls.gov/opub/ted/2015/median-weekly-earnings-by-education-gender-race-and-ethnicity-in-2014.htm.

a) What does the term *census* mean? Several good definitions are reported here: http://www.thefreedictionary.com/census.

The table reports information for several variables, both qualitative and quantitative. Use the details from the title, the source information, and the table to respond to each item below.

b) State the three qualitative variables along with the values of each one.

c) State the quantitative variable.

The graph below is one of the bar charts that can be created from the table's information. It is a "cluster" bar chart that provides information on three variables. The goal is to show the disparities in median weekly wages for the variable the census bureau calls "gender" within each educational attainment level category. Note that the gender bars touch within each education level but constant spacing is maintained between each education level. The vertical axis represents the quantitative variable median weekly wages. A similar graph could be produced to show racial disparities.

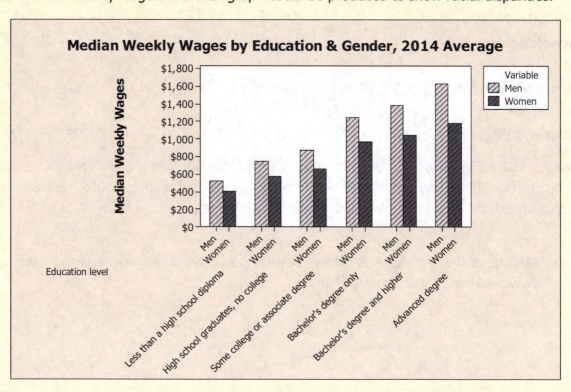

d) Could the information in the table be shown appropriately in a pie chart? Explain.

e) What disparity is immediately obvious between the median weekly wages between men and women across all education levels?

f) Using the values from the table, find the absolute and relative differences to compare the median weekly wages of women to men within the bachelor's degree education level. Remember to write appropriate self-contained contextual sentences for both measures.

3) The distribution of the 2007 estimated median SAT scores for 52 US public universities with student populations of 15,000 to 20,000 students is shown in the graph that follows. The data were reported by The Education Trust. http://www.collegeresults.org/.

a) Identify the variable and the individuals.

- Variable:

- Individuals:

b) Use the information from the opening description and part **a** to label the graph. The labelling should allow for self-contained communication of relevant details.

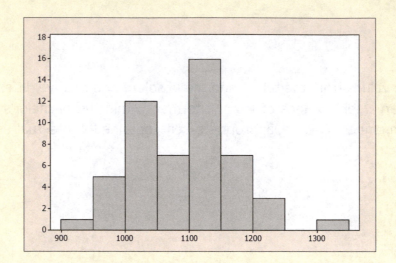

Respond to each of the following using self-contained sentences. Remember that context is critical!

c) Describe the basic shape of the distribution along with variable values of peaks and any internal gaps.

d) Describe the center of the distribution including both position in terms of ordered observations and variable value as well as the spread.

e) Identify any obvious outliers in the distribution.

f) How do you expect the values of the mean and the median to compare? Explain.

g) Based on the shape of the distribution, which set of number summaries would you suggest we use? Explain your answer.

h) Would your choice of summaries change if the outlying university was removed? Explain.

i) What would happen to the value of the mean without the outlier? Explain.

j) How would the values of the mean and the median compare without that outlier? Explain.

4) The distribution of the number of infant deaths per 1,000 live births between 2010 and 2015 for 241 countries is shown below. The data is from UNdata, a service of the United Nations. (http://data.un.org/)

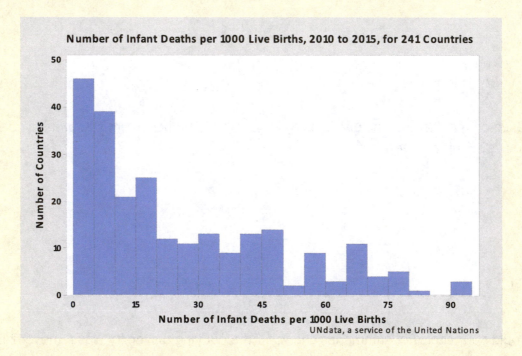

Number of Infant Deaths per 1000 Live Births, 2010 to 2015, for 241 Countries

UNdata, a service of the United Nations

Respond to each of the following using self-contained sentences. Remember that context is critical!

a) What is the variable? (Remember the variable must be defined for one individual.)

b) Who/what are the individuals? Do these individuals represent a sample or a population?

c) Describe the basic shape of the distribution along with variable values of peaks and any internal gaps.

d) Describe the center of the distribution including both position in terms of ordered observations and variable value as well as the spread.

e) Identify any obvious outliers in the distribution.

f) What set of number summaries (mean and standard deviation or median and the rest of the five-number summary) would you suggest for this variable's distribution? Explain your reasoning.

g) How do you expect the values of mean and median to compare? Explain.

5) The boxplots of the poverty rates (the percentage of the state population living in poverty) of all of the states in each of the four US Census Bureau's census regions are shown below. Remember units as you respond to questions.

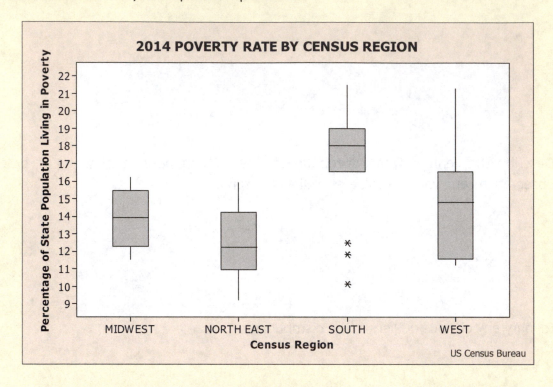

a) Which region has the most variability (widest spread) in poverty rates when outliers are included? The poverty rates in the _____ region go from about _____ to _____, when outliers are included.

b) Which region has the most variability (widest spread) in poverty rates when outliers are not considered? The poverty rates in the _____ region go from about _____ to _____.

c) Which region has the highest poverty rates overall? The poverty rates in the _____ region go from about _____ to _____ when outliers are ignored. The outlying states in this region have poverty rates that are much _____ than the rest of the poverty rates in the region.

d) List the census regions in order from highest to lowest median poverty level. Include the approximate median value next to the regions name.

6) The following data represent the poverty rate (the percentage of the state population living in poverty) of the states in the US Census Bureau's southern census region. Complete all work in this problem manually, then check your answers using your calculator. (Calculators do not provide the five-number summary positions.)

| 19.3 18.9 12.5 17.7 16.5 18.3 19.1 19.8 10.1 21.5 17.2 16.6 18 18.3 17.2 11.8 18.3 |

a) Find the five-number summary position (in terms of ordered observation) and value of the poverty rates in this census region. Place the position below the line and the value on the line.

	Minimum	First Quartile	Median	Third Quartile	Maximum
Value:	_____	_____	_____	_____	_____
Position:					

b) Write a contextual interpretation of the third quartile.

c) Find the mean and standard deviation of the poverty rates in this census region. Remember that these values represent the poverty rate of ALL southern region states. Use the appropriate symbols to label.

d) Create a frequency distribution for the data. Use a class width of 2%, starting the first class at 10%.

7) The following data represent the poverty rate (the percentage of the state population living in poverty) of the states in the US Census Bureau's western census region. Complete all work in this problem manually, then check your answers using your calculator. (Calculators do not provide the five-number summary positions.)

11.2 18.2 16.4   12   11.4 14.8 15.4 15.2 21.3 16.6 11.7 13.2 11.2

a) Find the five-number summary position (in terms of ordered observation) and value of the poverty rates in this census region. Place the position below the line and the value on the line.

	Minimum	First Quartile	Median	Third Quartile	Maximum
Value:	_____	_____	_____	_____	_____
Position:					

b) Write a contextual interpretation of the first quartile.

c) Find the mean and standard deviation of the poverty rates in this census region. Remember that these values represent the poverty rate of ALL western region states. Use the appropriate symbols to label.

d) Create a frequency distribution for the data. Use a class width of 2%, starting the first class at 10%.

CRITICAL NOTE: THOUGH THE SAT SCORES (WHICH ARE SCORES FROM STANDARDIZED TESTS) WERE STANDARDIZED, MOST DISTRIBUTIONS HAVE NOT BEEN STANDARDIZED. INCLUDING "STANDARDIZED" IN YOUR SENTENCE RESPONSES TO THE NORMAL DISTRIBUTION PROBLEMS THAT FOLLOW WOULD BE INCORRECT!

8) The distribution of baby girls' birthweights in a certain population is approximately normally distributed with a mean of mean of 7.13 pounds and a standard deviation of 1.07 pounds. Use the 68-95-99.7 rule to answer the questions that follow. Remember the variable label and description as well as the self-contained sentence responses.

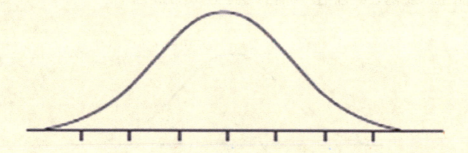

a) What percentage of baby girls is expected to weigh less 6.06 pounds at birth? Less than 3.92 pounds at birth?

b) What percentage of baby girls is expected to weigh more than 8.2 pounds at birth?

c) What percentage of baby girls is expected to weigh between 4.99 pounds and 10.34 pounds at birth?

9) The distribution of baby girls' birthweights in a certain population is approximately normally distributed with a mean of mean of 7.13 pounds and a standard deviation of 1.07 pounds. Use the 68-95-99.7 rule to answer the questions that follow. Remember the variable label and description as well as the self-contained sentence responses.

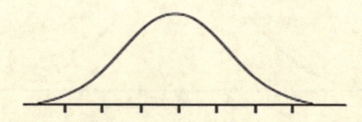

a) What percentage of baby girls is expected to weigh less than 4.99 pounds at birth?

b) What percentage of baby girls is expected to weigh more than 9.27 pounds at birth? More than 4.99 pounds at birth?

c) What percentage of baby girls is expected to weigh between 3.92 pounds and 9.27 pounds at birth?

The US Centers for Disease Control and Prevention recommends that healthcare providers use the World Health Organization's (WHO) growth charts for infants from birth through 24 months. These charts are reported on a metric scale. Research supports that the exact distribution of birthweights depends on many factors including gender and ethnicity. The WHO birthweight chart for baby girls appears to follow a distribution of birthweights that are approximately normally distributed with a mean of 3,232 grams and a standard deviation of 490 grams. **Use the standard normal table to answer the questions that follow**. Show ALL appropriate mathematics steps, notations, and interpret the results in context. Use the information presented above and complete each of the following steps for problems 10, 11, and 12.

a) Sketch the distribution, labeling the variable and shading the area associated the indicated probability.

b) Complete all mathematical steps as demonstrated in the examples. Use appropriate notation.

c) Write a self-contained response to the question. Remember the questions are in different forms and require different responses. Then respond to: Is outcome typical or unusual? Be sure to support your statement.

10) Babies born with birthweights below 2,500 grams are considered to have low birthweights. What proportion of baby girls is likely to born with a low birthweight?

11) What percentage of baby girls is expected to have birthweights between 3,000 grams and 3,500 grams?

12) What is the probability that a randomly selected baby girl will have a birthweight of at least 3,600 grams?

A recent California study of a large number of infant boys found that their birthweights followed a distribution of weights that were approximately normally distributed with a mean of 3,455 grams and a standard deviation of 464 grams. Use the standard normal table to answer the questions that follow. Show ALL appropriate mathematics steps, notations, and interpret the results in context. Use the information presented above and complete each of the following steps for problems 13, 14, and 15.

a) Sketch the distribution, labeling the variable and shading the area associated the indicated probability.

b) Complete all mathematical steps as demonstrated in the examples. Use appropriate notation.

c) Write a self-contained response to the question. Remember the questions are in different forms and require different responses. Then respond to: Is outcome typical or unusual? Be sure to support your statement.

13) Babies born with birthweights below 2,500 grams are considered to have low birthweights. What proportion of the baby boys from the California study was likely born with a low birthweight?

14) What percentage of baby boys from the California study likely had birthweights between 3,000 grams and 3,500 grams?

15) What is the probability that a randomly selected baby boy chosen from those in the California study would have a birthweight of at least 3,600 grams?

CHAPTER 5
Using Data to Make Sense of the World

CHAPTER OBJECTIVES

Upon completion of this chapter, the student should be able to

□ Identify and describe, in context, the individual(s), variable, population, sample, parameter, statistic, and sampling plan, when given a brief study description.

□ Report and justify your decision of the type of study (observational or experimental), when provided a study description. If an experiment, identify the control and treatment groups and type of blinding.

□ Determine the confidence interval and write a complete self-contained three-part confidence statement when provided with a relevant study description. Respond to questions based on this interpretation.

□ Write the complete self-contained contextual hypothesis text analysis (including the p-value explanation, statistical significance discussion, the complete conclusion, and question response) when provided with a brief description of hypothesis test results.

In today's "connected" world, we are constantly inundated by information based upon "data" that we then use to make decisions. In making these decisions, it is critical that we distinguish quality data from questionable data as well as understand any limitations of the data that might impact those decisions. The next few sections will provide some foundational tools for understanding data sets, the data collection process and finally the fundamentals of making statistical decisions or inference.

5.1 DATA FUNDAMENTALS—REVISITING AND ADDING TO BASIC STATISTICAL TERMINOLOGY AND DEFINITIONS

The need for data typically grows out of a need to answer questions. The key to collecting quality data that will answer those questions is the ability to precisely define the "objects" of interest along with the characteristics about those objects that are needed/desired. Some of the terms listed below were also seen in Chapter 4.

- An **individual** (also called **unit** or **subject** or **case**) is one of the "objects" or "entities" to be studied. An individual might be a person or animal but could also be an entity like a part coming off an assembly line, or a city, country, state, and so forth.
- A **population** is the complete set of individuals of interest. It is the entire group of individuals for which information is desired or needed. It is impossible, or at the very least impractical, to gather information for the entire population.
- The **sample** is the subset of individuals drawn from all individuals in the population for which information is actually gathered. The **sample size** is simply the number of individuals in the sample.
- A **variable** is a characteristic that is measured or recorded for one individual. The variable is always defined at the individual level. Variables can be either *qualitative* (gender, race, locality, educational attainment, etc.) or *quantitative* (age, number of children, weight, etc.)

  - It is typical to gather data on multiple variables simultaneously. (For example, most surveys ask multiple questions; when a patient visits a physician multiple key pieces of information like weight, blood pressure, body temperature, etc., are typically recorded.)

- The **parameter** is a numerical summary of a variable measured on the entire population. Studies are typically designed to estimate the value of the parameter, as typically the value of the parameter is unknown and cannot be directly determined. The distinction between the parameter (description) and the value of a parameter (the numerical value of the parameter calculated from all individuals in the entire population) is CRITICAL.
- The **statistic** is a numerical summary of a variable measured on a sample. The **value of the statistic** depends entirely on the sample selected and is expected to vary from one sample to the next. The distinction between the statistic (description) and the value of a statistic (the numerical value of the statistic calculated from one sample of individuals drawn from the entire population of individuals) is CRITICAL.

Note: When asked to **describe the parameter or statistic you provide a verbal description**, NOT a numerical value. When a numerical value is required, you will be specifically asked for the "value."

EXAMPLE 1: A poll was conducted in early 2016 to determine the percentage of US likely voters that would vote along party lines regardless of the party nominee. The poll results were based on the responses of 1,405 randomly selected US likely voters. In this one sample, 40% said they would vote along party lines regardless of the party nominee.

In this example,

- An **individual** is *one US likely voter*.
- The **population** is *all US likely voters*.
- The **sample** is the *US likely voters that responded to the poll*. The **sample size** was 1,405.
- The one **variable** that we know was recorded for each responding likely voter was *whether they would vote along party lines regardless of the nominee*. This is a qualitative variable.
- The **parameter** is the *percentage of all US likely voters that would vote along party lines regardless of the party nominee*. The **value of this parameter** is *unknown* and our sample will only provide one estimate of the value.

  - This is a situation where it would be impossible to gather responses from the population of ALL likely voters, so estimates from samples really are the only data-gathering option.

- The **statistic** is the *percentage of likely voters responding to the poll that indicate they would vote along party lines regardless of the party nominee*. The **value of the statistic** for this one sample is *40%*.

  - But remember, if some different random sample of 1,405 US likely voters was obtained and the same variable recorded for each respondent, it is quite likely that the statistic value would be different, even though the statistic description would remain the same!

EXAMPLE 2: Suppose that there is a need to answer questions about or describe National Football League (NFL) football teams and we have been charged with designing the study that will gather the data. We begin by defining each of the basic elements:

- An **individual** would be a *National Football League football team*.

Now we would need to **define the population**, exactly which NFL teams? On the surface this seems pretty straightforward but the number of teams, the location of teams, and even the name of teams have all changed over time. *So, which NFL teams really are of interest; are we looking for some historical perspective or are we seeking information about current teams? The overarching goal of the study is critical in determining the population and the variables.* But for now, let us just concern ourselves with the current NFL teams.

➢ The **population** is the *current 32 National Football League teams*.

Before we actually start gathering data, we would need to **decide is whether to gather information on all 32 teams or only part of them**. *If we decide to gather information only on SOME of the teams, then*

➢ The **sample** would be *the current NFL teams for which data were actually collected.*

Already we see that being precise in our descriptions is absolutely key to creating quality data; otherwise we, and others using the information, are left making assumptions which may or may not be accurate.

The next step is to **identify the specific pieces of information that must be gathered** about each individual (team). **What will our variables be?** For NFL teams, the list of potential variables is very long, so only a few regular season possibilities are suggested.

➢ **Potential qualitative variables** that could be recorded for each team are *conference* (AFC/NFC) and *division* (ACW/ACE/ACN/ACS/NCW/NCE/NCN/NCS).

- Typically, qualitative variables are summarized by **parameters/statistics** that are the percentage or proportion in a category. For the variables suggested here, however, the NFL has a set number of teams in each category, so noting things like the percentage of all NFL teams that are in the American Football Conference has little meaning since, by design, both conferences have 50% of the 32 teams.

➢ **Potential quantitative variables** that could be recorded for each team's regular season play might be the *number of touchdowns in 2015* and *total number of points scored in 2015*.

For the two listed quantitative variables, we might define the following **parameters** for all current NFL teams:

- *The average number of touchdowns per game for all NFL teams in 2015*

- *The average number of points scored per game for all NFL teams in 2015*

Since the NFL makes this data readily available for all teams, determining the value of these parameters could be easily accomplished. This also means that though we could choose to record information for only a few teams and thus calculate values of sample statistics, this is a situation where population information IS available to use. In this situation, working with actual population information makes sense.

YOUR TURN 1: Suppose that James Madison University (JMU) plans to contact 400 randomly selected entering JMU freshmen and will conduct a survey among those that agree to participate. Among the things that they wish to estimate from the resulting data are the percentage of entering freshmen that had access to vehicles that they would have brought with them to school if they were allowed to park them on campus and the average distance that entering freshmen travel from home to JMU (in miles). Complete the following: In this study,

a) An **individual** will be:

b) The **population** will be:

c) The **sample** will be:

d) The desired **sample size** is:_____. (The actual sample size depends on how many actually agree to participate.) *THIS IS THE ONLY ANSWER THAT IS A NUMBER!*

e) The qualitative **variable** that we know must be recorded for each individual is

f) The quantitative **variable** that we know must be recorded for each individual is

g) JMU hopes to estimate the values of these two **parameters**:

h) The descriptions of the two corresponding **statistics** are:

5.2 DATA COLLECTION—OVERVIEW OF STATISTICAL STUDY TYPES AND SAMPLING METHODS

In general, studies that lead to data fall into two categories: **observational studies** and **experiments**. Both types of studies require great care in defining the population and variables as well as in designing the method of data collection necessary to arrive at data that might lead to meaningful conclusions. Sadly, it is often up to us to determine whether the results we see and hear about in the media are meaningful because many studies that are published are based on highly flawed methods or the media coverage leaves out critical details. Just because a study is published, just because a study uses a large "sample" or involves experimentation, we cannot assume the study or resulting data are statistically useful.

5.2.1 Observational Studies

In an **observational study**, researchers observe or measure and record characteristics of the observed or sampled individuals but do not attempt to influence or modify these characteristics.

➢ Polls, surveys, data resulting from direct observation and recording of characteristics about the observed individuals, data gathered from sampling existing records, and so forth, are examples of observational studies.

➢ The usefulness of the data collected from observational studies depends on how accurately the sample "represents" the population. Key is the careful ***random selection*** of the sampled individuals from a well-defined population.

➢ The big concern with observational studies is the lack of control of over variables that influence results but that were not identified and/or not measured as part of the data collection.

The vast majority of statistical studies gather data from sampled individuals in order to draw conclusions about some larger defined population. For these conclusions about the population to be meaningful, the individuals that make up the sample must be ***representative*** of that population and the definition of the population must be well defined.

➢ A truly **representative sample** would have the same characteristics of the population in the same proportions as they exist in the population. Since such perfection is not possible, we hope for samples that have the characteristics of the population in similar proportions to those in the population.

➢ Though it is impossible to guarantee a representative sample, the best way to achieve one is through the use of a ***random sampling plan*** to <u>select individuals from the population</u> that will become the <u>study's sample</u>. (The underlined portions here are important. If the sampled individuals are not actually chosen from the identified population, we cannot expect the sample to be representative of that population, even if the sampling method WAS apparently random.)

➢ Although the resulting samples are often called "*random samples*," it is actually the organized method of selection that is random and, as such, allows the probability of selecting each potential sample from the population to be calculated in advance.

Random Sampling Plans—high-level descriptions of some common plans

➢ **Simple random sampling**: The sample of individuals is chosen in such a way that every sample of a given size has an equal chance of being selected. We start with a ***sampling frame***, a numbered list of all members of the population, and then use a random number generator or similar tool to select the individuals from the list.

  • In real life, this method is rarely employed though it is the most typical method identified in the inference problems of introductory statistics textbooks.

➢ **Systematic sampling**: Again, starting with the sampling frame, a simple "system" is used to choose the sample after picking a random starting place . . . such as selecting every 10th or every 50th member of the population. Listed individuals should not have a systematic order.

The two random selection methods listed above can easily leave out individuals with characteristics that have proportionally small representation within the population. (For example, if only 1% of the population is of a certain ethnicity, a sample from this population might easily have no representation of the ethnic group.)

➢ **Stratified sampling**: This method is employed when there are concerns or expectations that there are differences among distinct subgroups of similar individuals, or *strata*, within a population. *After first identifying the subgroups*, a random sample (possibly simple) is selected from within each subgroup. The resulting sample consists of all the individuals selected from each of the subgroups.

- The strength of this method is that it guarantees representation of all the identified subgroups, even if the subgroup sizes within the population vary dramatically. So, if a population is made up of individuals within distinct racial groups of varying size and there is reason to suspect that results may vary by those racial groups, stratifying by race will guarantee that each racial group is represented in the final sample.

➢ **Cluster sampling**: This method also involves the identification of subgroups but these subgroups (clusters) are not made up of similar individuals. Individuals within the subgroups (the clusters) are often quite diverse but the "grouping/clustering" is often based on a common circumstance/situation, that is, all people on a given flight from point A to point B would be a cluster, all people living on the same floor of the same dormitory would be a cluster, and so forth. Similar *clusters* are identified (like all the flights that go from point A to point B), some predetermined number of clusters are randomly selected and then all the individuals from those selected clusters become the sample.

Common Nonrandom Sampling Plans—we cannot use the results of these sampling plans to draw statistically valid conclusions about any population.

➢ **Convenience sampling**: The sample is made up of those individuals that the researcher chooses to include because they are easy or convenient to access. Such individuals are often in a common location or have a common group membership, such as people who happen to be in the same class. In cases like that described, this approach necessarily leads to a sample of individuals that clearly have at least some common characteristics and therefore do not reflect the opinions of any broader population.

➢ **Voluntary response or self-selected sampling**: The researchers issue a general appeal to some population via e-mail, web survey, or television and wait for individuals to respond. Those individuals that respond to the appeal, who are often those with the strongest opinions, become the sample. Since the results over represent those with the strongest opinions, they do not reflect the opinions of any broader population.

EXAMPLE 3: Identify the type of sampling plan being used to study a school library issue in each scenario described below.

➢ An administrator obtains a sample of JMU students by randomly selecting 15 students from each class: Freshman, Sophomore, Junior, and Senior. stratified

➢ An administrator uses a random number generator to obtain 60 numbers then matches those numbers to those on a numbered roster of JMU students, thus identifying 60 students to form the sample. simple random

➢ An administrator speaks to the first 100 students coming through the back entrance of Roop Hall on Monday morning. convenience

➢ An administrator takes a numbered list of enrolled JMU students and then selects the sample by randomly choosing one student at random from among the first 100 and then taking every 100th name on the roster thereafter until they have 60 students. systematic

➢ The administrator sends e-mails to all JMU students and the first 100 students that respond form the sample. voluntary response

➢ The administrator identifies the three courses within each department (Mathematics, English, Biology, etc.) that have the most diverse students, and then selects one of those courses at random from each department. All the students in the selected course from each department become the sample. cluster

Regardless of the sampling method:

➢ A study can be successful only if the sample is representative of the population.

➢ Even if a sample is chosen in the best possible way (using random sampling), it is still just a sample (as opposed to the entire population). We can never be *certain that a sample is representative* of the population. Some samples will simply give results far away from the truth about the population. *Random selection allows the researcher to quantify how likely it is that the sample results will be close to the parameter value*. Nonrandom samples do not allow such calculation.

➢ In general, larger random samples are more likely to be given estimates close to the truth about the population . . . though large is not nearly as big as one might think. Random samples of only around 1,000 individuals are very successfully employed in estimating proportions/percentages for the entire population of the United States with very statistically accurate results. MUCH smaller samples are successfully employed for averages.

YOUR TURN 2: Identify the type of sampling plan:

a) To gather data about MATH 220 students, five Monday/Wednesday/Friday sections are randomly selected along with four Tuesday/Thursday sections. Surveys are then conducted among all students in those nine sections.

b) To gather data about the importance of athletic event attendance to the undergraduate experience at JMU, surveys are conducted with 200 students in attendance at the first home football game of the season.

5.2.2 Experimental Studies

In an **experiment**, researchers apply a treatment (or treatments) to the participants and then measure relevant characteristics to see if the treatment(s) had effect(s). In an experiment, the researchers actively intervene in order to influence/change characteristics.

> A particular strength of a well-designed experiment is that it can give evidence of cause and effect, which is very difficult with even the best observational studies. This strength lies in the ability to control (within limitations) for other "variables" that impact results.
> Always of concern is that when humans are involved, particularly in medical experiments, the participants themselves are volunteers.
> Randomness is still critical but is typically achieved through **random assignment** of participants to treatment groups rather than random selection of individuals from the population.
> The **treatment group** in an experiment is the group of study participants who receive the treatment being tested.
> The **control group** in an experiment is the group of study participants who do *not* receive the treatment being tested.

Since people studied in experiments are nearly always volunteers, it is important for the treatment and control groups to be randomly assigned and to be treated alike in all respects except for treatment assignment. Note that it is also possible to have more than two treatment groups.

> A **placebo** lacks the active ingredients of a treatment being tested in a study, but is identical in appearance to the treatment. Thus, study participants cannot distinguish the placebo from the real treatment. Placebos are often used to "treat" the control group though existing treatments are also employed.
> The **placebo effect** refers to the situation in which patients improve simply because they believe they are receiving a useful treatment.
> An experiment is **single-blind** if the participants do not know whether they are members of the treatment group or members of the control group, but the experimenters (people administering the treatments) do know (or vice versa, if the experimenters interacting with the participants do not know the group membership).
> An experiment is **double-blind** if neither the participants nor the experimenters know who belongs to the treatment group and who belongs to the control group.

EXAMPLE 4: A physician believes he has come up with a great new headache treatment. From among his patients, he and his staff choose and convince 100 of his patients with long histories of difficult-to-treat headaches to participate in a small initial study. Although he will analyze the data, he has his office manager randomly assign the 100 patients to two groups so that he does not know which patients are in which group. One group will take his new treatment as soon as they notice their headache, whereas the second group will take a standard dose of ibuprofen at the first sign of a headache. The patients have been provided with all study medications that are identical in every way except for the active ingredients.

In this study

➢ The **sample** is made up of the physician's 100 patient volunteers who had long histories of difficult-to-treat headaches.
➢ The study is an **experiment** because the researcher is actively intervening with treatments in order to observe the impact.
➢ The **treatment group** is the patients randomly assigned to take the physician's new treatment as soon as they notice a headache.
➢ The **control group** is the patients randomly assigned to take a standard dose of ibuprofen as soon as they notice a headache.
➢ This experiment is **double-blind** because the physician does not know which patients are in each group and the patients themselves do not know which medication they are taking because the study medications appear identical to them.

YOUR TURN 3: Suppose that a pair of educators wishes to gauge the effectiveness of online quizzes in improving students' daily preparation for class. The scores of daily in-class quizzes for students in two groups in the same course will be compared. Students in two sections will be assigned to one of two groups: one group will have daily assigned readings and be required to complete an online quiz prior to in-class coverage of new material, whereas the other group will be assigned the readings without the online quiz requirement. The faculty member assigned to grade the daily in-class quizzes will not know the group membership. Complete the following: In this study,

a) The sample is:

b) The treatment group is:

c) The control group is:

d) This experiment is _____ blind because

5.3 STATISTICAL INFERENCE: FROM SAMPLE TO POPULATION

With a basic understanding of both statistical study terminology and study design, we are now ready to move on to what *Statistics* is really about: using sample information to draw conclusions or to make *inferences* about the population. We know studying the entire population is rarely possible except in cases where the population is very small and easily accessible. Instead of collecting data on the entire population, we record or take variable measurements from a subset of individuals in a carefully selected sample drawn from the population of interest. Using those data values to calculate the value of sample statistic (like a sample mean, $\bar{x}$, or sample proportion, $\hat{p}$) to infer or make conclusions about the value of a population parameter like μ (population mean) or p (population proportion).

5.3.1 Key Ideas behind Statistical Inference

For all statistical inference, *randomness*, through random selection or random assignment, is critical to the probability that is the foundation of the mathematics that underlie the inferential procedures!

➤ *Before trusting any data as a basis for statistical inference, be sure the study and data collection procedures were well-designed and implemented.*

➤ The **predictable behavior** of sample statistic values in repeated random samples from the same population is the basis of the science that allows probabilities to be calculated and decisions to be made.

➤ **Probability** is a mathematically derived numerical measure of the "chance" occurrence of an outcome in repeated random samples from the population under identical conditions. It quantifies how likely a given outcome is, if ONLY chance is controlling the outcomes of different samples. Probability values are always between 0 and 1. Both 0 and 1 are valid probabilities.

➤ In real life, it is exceptionally rare that more than one sample is selected. But, all our decisions are based on what is EXPECTED to happen IF many random samples were selected. The results of a single sample are sufficient because of the previously mentioned predictable behavior of sample statistic values based on repeated random samples from the population.

EXAMPLE 5: *What is Predictable Behavior?* Imagine that you had the time to randomly select 500 samples from a population on four separate occasions. Further, imagine that you know that 50% of the population have a known characteristic. The first time you do the samples you use a sample size of $n = 100$, the second occasion $n = 500$, the third $n = 1,000$, and on the fourth $n = 5,000$. Realistically, do you think this can really be accomplished in any reasonable fashion? Probably not.

Luckily, computers and software can simulate this process. Using Minitab 16 Statistical software, four sets of 500 samples were selected from a population where $p = 0.5$. The size of the samples in the four sets were $n = 100$, $n = 500$, $n = 1,000$, and $n = 5,000$, just as stated previously. For each sample in each set, the value of the sample proportion was calculated. The graphic facing this discussion shows the distributions of Sample Proportion Values for the four sets of 500 samples from a population where the parameter of interest is known to have the value $p = 0.5$. All four graphs have an x-axis scale from 0.3 to 0.7 to allow us to see how the spread changes.

➢ In the upper left corner, the distribution of sample proportion values uses samples of size 100. It is clearly fairly symmetric and bell shaped with a bit of a flattened top. The sample proportion values appear centered on 0.5 and spread from 0.32 to 0.65.

➢ In the upper right corner, the distribution of sample proportion values uses samples of size 500. It is clearly symmetric and bell shaped. The sample proportion values are centered on 0.5 and spread from 0.43 to 0.57.

➢ In the lower left corner, the distribution of sample proportion values uses samples of size 1,000. It is clearly symmetric and bell shaped. The sample proportion values are centered at 0.5 and spread from 0.44 to 0.55.

➢ In the lower right corner, the distribution of sample proportion values uses samples of size 5,000. It is clearly symmetric and bell shaped. The sample proportion values are centered at 0.5 and spread from 0.48 to 0.52.

The point of this graphical illustration is to show the *predictable the behavior of statistic values* (the sample proportions) when samples are randomly chosen from the population. In all four cases, the sample proportion values cluster in a symmetric, bell-shaped pattern around the stated population value. Note that this clustering about the parameter value would happen EVEN if we did not know the parameter's value! So regardless of the sample size, the statistic values are centered on the true value of the parameter, BUT as the sample size increases the spread of the statistic values gets smaller.

We can clearly see that the sample proportion values vary less for larger samples than they did for smaller samples. But the differences in spread were quite minor as the sample size increased from 500 to 1,000. In fact, a graph for samples of size 2,500 was also completed but the change in spread was so minor in comparison to that for samples of 1,000 that it was not included.

It takes quite dramatic changes in sample size (at least four times) to have big impact on the variability/spread. This is one reason that samples of 1,000 to 1,500 individuals are typical in polling. To see real impact on the variability would require large increases in sample sizes (to around 4,000/5,000) and thus increase the time required to collect and process the data and would dramatically increase costs. The small decreases in variability are simply not worth the increased time and cost.

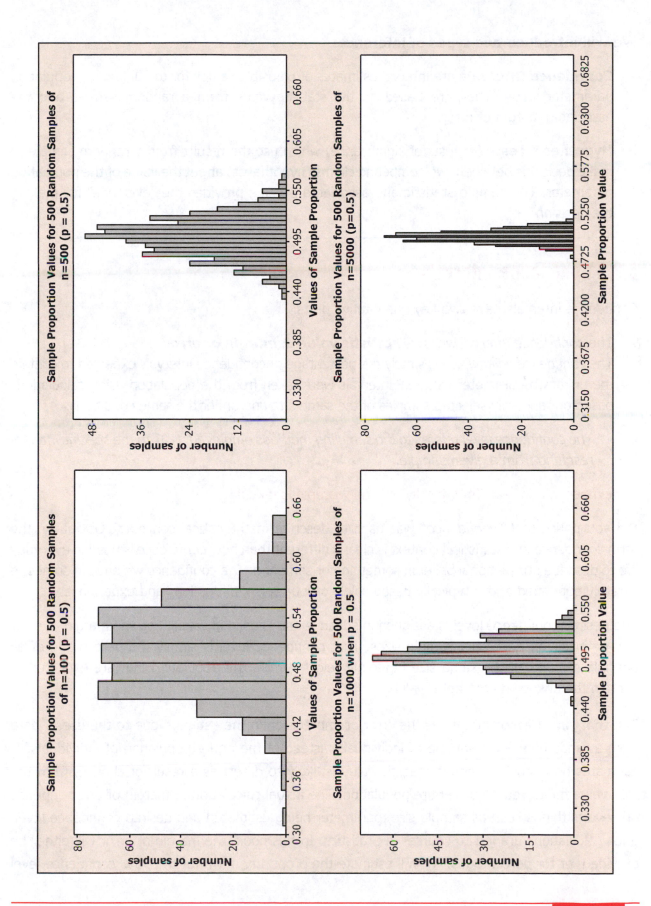

We will introduce two types of inference:

➢ **Confidence Intervals** are interval estimates of plausible values for the unknown population parameter value. They are based on the statistic value from a random sample and the associated margin of error.

➢ **Hypothesis Tests** (or tests of significance) which use the results from a random sample to make decisions between two competing claims (hypotheses) about the value of the population parameter. The sample statistic and associated *p*-value provides the "evidence" for making the decision.

5.3.2 Confidence Intervals

Confidence intervals have two key quantitative parts:

➢ The *confidence interval* which is ***statistic value ± margin of error***
➢ The *confidence level* which is simply the percentage of confidence intervals expected to contain the unknown parameter value **IF** intervals were taken from the population using calculations based on randomly selected samples of the same size and under the same conditions.

- *The confidence level relates to the sampling methods employed, NOT to the specific interval resulting from a given sample.*

Remember that in real life, typically only one sample is taken!

Did you notice that "*confidence*" was used to describe mathematical concepts? Obviously, the term *confidence* in a statistical context is clearly different than how *confidence* is used in everyday life to describe our personal belief in something or someone. The confidence we have in someone is rarely quantified and is typically based solely on our personal opinions and experiences.

The desired confidence level is assigned in advance and is used in calculating the margin of error and determining necessary sample sizes. That confidence level is simply the percentage of all possible samples of the same size randomly selected from the population that are expected to contain the unknown parameter value.

The **margin of error** quantifies the error or imprecision in the estimate due to the use of data from a random selected sample of individuals instead of the entire population of individuals. It estimates how much a sample statistic value is likely to differ, as a result of chance, from the true value measured on the entire population. The actual calculation of margin of error depends on several things such as sample size, parameter being estimated and desired confidence level. Such calculations are left to courses in Statistics. In this book, the margin of error will either be provided, or for percentages, we will estimate the proportion form for the 95% confidence level by using $\dfrac{1}{\sqrt{n}}$ (***n*** = sample size) and then convert to percentage form. Margin of error and related confidence intervals must only be calculated for samples resulting from random sampling plans; otherwise they are meaningless.

Often media reports will fail to mention the confidence level even though they report the margin of error. This omission is common because reputable polling organizations (Gallup, Roper, Pew, and major news organizations) nearly always use 95% confidence in calculating the margin of error. Poll reports from reputable polling organizations will provide confidence levels if they are not 95% and will clearly indicate when their polls were not conducted randomly so that we know that inference is not possible! Sadly, this notification is typically not provided when data are collected by less reputable organizations.

For now, think of 95% *confidence* as follows: If a poll were repeated 20 times with 20 different samples of the same size that were randomly selected from the population, 19 of the 20 polls (95% of the polls) would be expected to provide an interval of values that contains the true value of the population parameter.

➢ Note that this implies that 1 of the 20 intervals calculated is expected to NOT contain the value of the parameter.
➢ Since we typically do not know the value of the parameter, we have no way to judge whether the one interval that was calculated from our one sample was one of the 95% of all possible confidence intervals that would contain the parameter value or one of the 5% that would not contain the parameter value.
➢ Every time a confidence interval is constructed, we take a risk of being incorrect in our conclusion. With 95% confidence, about 5% of the decisions made about the population parameter from well-constructed samples will be incorrect.

EXAMPLE 6: A nationwide poll of 2002 American adults, conducted in July 2015, by Pew Research Center, reported that 57% of the respondents answered "favor" to the question, "Please tell me if you would favor or oppose a ban on the sale of assault style weapons?" The margin of error was 2.5 percentage points. Would you claim that a majority of Americans support such a law? http://www.pewresearch.org/

Describe the statistic, give the statistic value, find the confidence interval, what parameter is expected to be in the interval and then answer the question, including reasoning.

➢ Statistic: the percentage of the responding Americans that said they favored a ban on the sale of assault style weapons.
➢ Statistic value: 57%
➢ Confidence interval: 54.5%–59.5%
➢ Parameter: the percentage of all American adults that favored a ban on the sale of assault style weapons. (Said cannot be used in the parameter description because the entire population did not respond to the question.)

> Question response: Yes, we can claim that in July 2015, a majority of Americans favored the ban on assault weapon sales because the entire confidence interval lies above 50%.

Once we have identified all the key information, it is now time to _interpret the results of the study for a general audience_. As we do so, we must recognize that _the terms "confidence" or "confident" have VERY distinct statistical meaning_ that are critical to understanding the results of the study. Thus, it is critical that the interpretation address that meaning without using the terms that are sure to confuse the general audience. As always, we must assume that the reader of our interpretations likely does not have access to the opening paragraph information or the key information that was identified.

> **Confidence Statement** (the interpretation):
> By using a random sampling method that gives intervals that contain the value of the parameter to be estimated in 95% of the times they are used, we conclude that the true value of the <u>percentage of all American adults that favor a ban on the sale of assault style weapons</u>* is between 54.5% and 59.5%.
>
> ***Three key components of this statement**: The information prior to the comma explains the confidence level without introducing terminology that a general audience would not understand; the information after the comma states that we are making a conclusion about a precisely defined parameter and ends with the interval estimate of that parameter's plausible values._

*In a confidence statement, the parameter must be stated explicitly and separately from the interval values, just as underlined above. Your instructor may have a slightly different variation of the confidence statement so be sure you know their specific expectations!!!

YOUR TURN 4: In a nationwide poll of 2008 American adults in mid-April 2016 by Pew Research Center (http://www.pewresearch.org/), 41% of the respondents indicated that they feel that the United States does too much in helping solve world problems. Use this information to respond to the following:

a) What is the statistic?

b) What is the statistic value?

c) What is the estimated 95% margin of error? (give in percent form with two decimal places)

d) What is the confidence interval?

e) What is the parameter? (Careful! *Indicated* cannot be used here!)

f) Give the appropriate and complete confidence statement.

g) Would you claim that a majority of American adults feel this way? Explain in terms of the confidence interval.

5.3.3 Hypothesis Tests or Tests of Significance

Hypothesis tests or tests of significance use the results of a study to make a decision between two competing claims (hypotheses) about the value of the population parameter or equality of corresponding parameters under two different conditions or in two populations.

The **null hypothesis**, typically labelled H_0, claims a specific value for a population parameter or, when comparing two groups or conditions, that the parameter under both conditions or in both groups are equal.

➤ When a parameter value is claimed, it is typically a well-known standard or historically accepted value.
➤ The null hypothesis represents the idea that nothing new is going on, nothing has changed, that whatever has been the accepted value of the parameter still is the value, or that there is no effect from what treatment has been applied.
➤ In the logic of making decisions in hypothesis testing, the null hypothesis is ALWAYS initially assumed to be true. This position is maintained unless the results from the sample gives evidence against it. The sample does not provide evidence for the null hypothesis, it either fails to give sufficient evidence to reject it or gives evidence to reject it.

Examples of null hypotheses:

H_0: *The true value of the mean body temperature of healthy humans is 98.6°F.*

H_0: *The proportion of patients who improve with the medication is the same as the proportion of patients that improve without the medication.*

The **alternative hypothesis**, labeled H_a OR H_1, claims that the value of the parameter has changed or, when comparing two groups or conditions, that the parameter under both conditions or in both groups are different in some way.

➤ The alternative hypothesis represents the idea that something has changed about the value of the parameter or that there is a treatment or group effect.

➤ The change that is claimed maybe in these forms (depending on situation):

• If testing whether there is simply a difference or change in the parameter value claimed in the null hypothesis, we would say "not equal" or "different from."

• If testing whether the parameter value might be higher than the value claimed in the null hypothesis, we would say "greater than."

• If testing whether the parameter value might be lower than the value claimed in the null hypothesis, we would say "less than."

➤ In the logic of making decisions in hypothesis testing, we reject the null hypothesis and conclude the alternative hypothesis when the results from the sample provide evidence against the null hypothesis. We never accept either the null or alternative hypotheses.

Examples of alternative hypotheses that might be used with the null hypotheses stated earlier:

H_a: The true value of the mean body temperature of healthy humans is less than 98.6°F.

H_a: The proportion of patients who improve with the medication is the higher than the proportion of patients that improve without the medication.

The hypotheses should ALWAYS be defined prior to data collection and should not change in response to what is seen in the sample(s). Sample results should never be used to decide the form of the alternative hypothesis.

Hypothesis Test Decisions: Reject or Fail to Reject

We consider the evidence provided by the sampled data and ***we reject the null hypothesis*** only if the evidence is convincing.

➤ This means a statistic value at least as extreme as the one calculated from the sample is so far from the parameter value stated in the null hypothesis, that we are convinced by the evidence that what was stated there is likely not true.

➤ Rejecting a null hypothesis is a strong conclusion. Rejection DOES NOT mean we have PROOF that the null hypothesis was wrong. Rejection DOES NOT mean we have PROVED that the alternative hypothesis is true.

If the sample does not provide such evidence, ***we fail to reject the null hypothesis***.

➤ This **does not** mean that the sample gave evidence **for** the null hypothesis, it simply lacked sufficient evidence to reject it.

> Failing to reject a null hypothesis is a weaker conclusion. Failing to reject DOES NOT mean we have PROOF that the null hypothesis is correct.

Note there are only two possible decisions (reject or fail to reject). ***Never accept*** either hypothesis! We cannot prove that the null hypothesis is true, we can only find statistical evidence that it is probably false, in which case we reject it.

Quantifying the Evidence from the Sample: The *p*-Value

The evidence provided by the sample is quantified by a ***p-value***.

> The *p*-value summarizes the evidence provided by the sample **against** the null hypothesis.
> The *p*-value is the probability of seeing a sample statistic value as extreme or more extreme than the one observed in the sample, if the value of the parameter hypothesized in the null hypothesis is true.
> A small *p*-value, close to zero, is strong evidence against the null hypothesis, leading us to reject H_0. It means the observed sample statistic value was so far from what was hypothesized in the null hypothesis that it would rarely occur, by chance alone, in random sampling.
> The fact that the observed sample statistic value represented a rare occurrence simply by chance, suggests that something other than chance led to the observed value.
> The smaller the *p*-value the stronger the evidence against the null hypothesis.
> A large *p*-value means we have little evidence against the null hypothesis, leading us to fail to reject H_0.

Determining If the Results Are Statistically Significant

A result from a statistical study is said to be **statistically significant** if the observed statistic value from the sample is unlikely to have occurred simply as a result of chance when the parameter value stated in the null hypothesis was true.

How do we decide if the results are statistically significant? What constitutes "unlikely to have occurred simply as a result of chance"? In this book, we will compare the *p*-value to the most commonly used levels of significance of 0.05 and 0.01.

> If the *p*-value is greater than 0.01 but less than 0.05, it indicates that the probability of observing a sample statistic value at least as extreme as the one resulting from the sample, if the hypothesized parameter value was accurate, is by chance alone 1 in 20 or less. This provides **sufficient** evidence to reject the null hypothesis and thus the study results are **statistically significant**.
> If the *p*-value is less than 0.01 it indicates that the probability of observing a sample statistic value at least as extreme as the one resulting from the sample, if the hypothesized parameter value was accurate, is by chance alone 1 in 100 or less. This provides **strong** evidence to reject the null hypothesis and thus the study results have **strong statistical significance**.

> If the *p*-value is greater than 0.05 it indicates that the probability of observing a sample statistic value at least as extreme as the one resulting from the sample, if the hypothesized parameter value was accurate, is by chance alone more than 1 in 20. Generally, this is **insufficient** evidence to reject the null hypothesis and thus the study results are **not statistically significant**.

Small p-values indicate that our sample had characteristics that were unusual to see in a sample when the null hypothesis is true. There is always the possibility that what was seen in these sample results occurred simply as a result of chance selection of the sample, not because there is some real change from what was stated in the null hypothesis! Meaning that because our observed p-value was less than 0.01 or 0.05, we could be making an incorrect decision when we reject! Every hypothesis test carries the risk of making the wrong decision, even when we complete every step perfectly!

CRITICAL IDEA: Just because results of a hypothesis test are deemed **statistically significant does not imply** that differences seen are **practically or substantively IMPORTANT**!

> If sample sizes are very large, differences that would be clearly trivial in real life may be statistically significant.
> If sample sizes are too small (as they can be in studies on rare diseases), differences that would clearly have large impact in real life might not be statistically significant.

EXAMPLE 7: A dog food manufacturer proudly claims that they "always give their customers more than what they pay for!" To prove their point, they state that the dog food in bags labelled "40 pounds" actually have a mean weight of 40.5 pounds. A consumer group suspects that the mean weight of all bags manufactured by the company is actually less than the 40.5 pounds advertised, and they plan to confront company executives if they can find evidence that the company is misleading their customers.

They plan to look at these hypotheses:

H_o: The true mean weight of "40-pound" bags from the dog food company is the 40.5 pounds advertised.

H_a: The true mean weight of "40-pound" bags from the dog food company is less than the 40.5 pounds advertised.

The group purchases 10 bags at random, finding a sample mean weight of 39 pounds. If the actual mean weight of the bags is as advertised, the probability of observing a sample mean weight at least as small as 39 pounds is 0.0008.

Does the sample indicate a problem with what was stated by the company and thus suggest the consumer group should confront the company executives? Outline the decision process by completing the four bolded items. (The italicized comments are not part of the answer; they are included here to help you understand the responses only.)

p-value explanation

If the true mean weight of "40-pound" bags from the dog food company is the 40.5 pounds advertised, the probability of observing a sample mean weight at least as small as 39 pounds is 0.0008.

Comments: Look carefully at this p-value explanation. It is very similar to earlier normal probability interpretations. Note that what comes prior to the comma is the null hypothesis, what follows the comma is the probability/p-value statement from the problem. This one was exactly the same but some may require a bit of rewording to make sense.

Statistical significance determination and reason

Since the *p*-value of 0.0008 is much smaller than 0.01, the study results have strong statistical significance.

Conclusion

The observational study provides strong evidence to conclude that the true mean weight of "40-pound" bags from the dog food company is less than the 40.5 pounds advertised, so the consumer group would reject the null hypothesis.

Comments: Look carefully at this explanation.

> The "strong evidence" reflects the 0.01 level of significance. (If it had been significant at the 0.05 level, "strong" would be replaced by "sufficient"; if it had not been statistically significant, "insufficient" would have replaced "strong.".)
> After "to conclude" you simply state the alternative hypothesis.
> The rejection is due to the statistically significant results. (If the results had not been statistically significant the consumer group would fail to reject the null hypothesis.)

Respond to the question

It appears that the mean weight of the dog food bags is below what the company advertised, so the consumer group has the evidence necessary to confront the company executives.

YOUR TURN 5: *The reported quantitative information is from William G. Cochran's. 1955. "Brief of Presidential Address: The 1954 Trial of the Poliomyelitis Vaccine in the United States." Biometrics 11:4. Accessed May 18, 2016.* http://www.jstor.org/stable/3001736.

In the 1940s and 1950s, though not a "common" disease, polio was an exceptionally feared and well-known disease that hit young children more dramatically than other age groups. Those who contracted and survived polio were often left paralyzed, including some that required lifelong mechanical help to breathe.

In 1954, one of the largest clinical trial studies ever conducted was initiated among young school-age children in the United States to test the effectiveness (not safety) of Salk's polio vaccine in fighting polio. There were actually several different trial arms of the study involving over one million first- through third-grade children. For a child to participate in the trial, their parents were required to sign informed consent documents volunteering their children's participation and approximately 69% of parents approached signed those forms.

In the randomized controlled trial arm of the study, 401,974 second-grade children from 11 states were randomly assigned to two injection groups. One group of 200,745 children received the Salk vaccine injection, whereas the remaining 201,229 children received a placebo injection. The researchers tested:

> H_o: *The proportions of children who get paralytic polio will be the same in vaccinated and nonvaccinated groups of children.*

> H_a: *The proportions of children who get polio will be lower in vaccinated children than in nonvaccinated children.*

Among the children in the Salk vaccine group, 33 developed paralytic polio. In the placebo group, 115 developed paralytic polio. The probability of observing a difference in the proportions of children developing paralytic polio at least as extreme as those seen in the trial, by chance alone, was 0.0000.

Did the randomized controlled trial provide convincing evidence that Salk's vaccine effectively prevented paralytic polio? Outline the decision process by completing the four bolded items.

a) ***p-value explanation***:

b) ***Statistical significance determination and reason***:

c) *Conclusion*:

d) *Respond to the question*:

YOUR TURN FINAL ANSWERS

1) a) An entering JMU freshman
   b) All entering JMU freshmen
   c) The entering freshmen that respond to the survey questions
   d) 400
   e) Whether or not the responding freshman has access to a vehicle that they would have brought to school if they were allowed to park them on campus
   f) The distance that the freshman travels from home to JMU, in miles
   g) The percentage of all entering freshmen that had access to vehicles that they would have brought with them to school if they were allowed to park them on campus and the average distance that all entering freshmen travel from home to JMU (in miles)
   h) The percentage of the responding entering freshmen that had access to vehicles that they would have brought with them to school if they were allowed to park them on campus and the average distance that the responding entering freshmen travel from home to JMU (in miles)

2) a) Cluster
   b) Convenience

3) a) The students in the two sections of the course that are assigned to groups
   c) The treatment group is made up of the students who have daily readings and are required to take an online quiz
   d) The control group is made up of the students who have daily readings but no online quizzes
   e) The experiment is single blind because students certainly know whether or not they are taking online quizzes, but the faculty member grading the in-class quizzes does not know the group membership.

4) a) The percentage of responding American adults that indicated that they feel that the United States does too much in helping solve world problems
   b) 41%
   c) $\dfrac{1}{\sqrt{2,008}} \approx 0.0223$, 2.23 percentage points
   d) 41% ± 2.23 percentage points, 38.77% to 43.23%
   e) The percentage of all American adults that feel that the United States does too much in helping solve world problems ("Indicated" cannot be used in the parameter description because the entire population did not respond to the question.)
   f) By using a random sampling method that gives intervals that contain the value of the parameter in 95% of the times they are used, we conclude that the true value of the percentage of all American adults that feel that the United States does too much in helping solve world problems is between 38.77% and 43.23%.

g) We cannot claim that a majority of Americans feel that the United States does too much in helping solve world problems because the entire confidence interval is below 50%. (The answer to this question is not about sample size as the size is far more than sufficient.)

5) a) If the proportions of children who get paralytic polio will be the same in vaccinated and nonvaccinated groups of children, probability of observing a difference in the proportions of children developing paralytic polio at least as extreme as those seen in the trial, by chance alone, was 0.0000. (Note that the portion of the sentence before the comma is the null hypothesis, what is after the comma is the description provided with the probability value.)

b) Since the *p*-value of 0.0000 is much smaller than 0.01, the study has strong statistical significance.

c) The experimental study provided strong evidence to conclude that the proportions of children who get polio will be lower in vaccinated children than in non-vaccinated children. The null hypothesis would be rejected. With results significant at the 0.01 level, the randomized controlled trial provided very convincing evidence that Salk's vaccine effectively prevented paralytic polio.

- **Chapter Terminology**: *If you do not know the meaning, record it here.*

- *Individual (Case/Subject)*

- *Variable*

- *Population*

- *Sample*

- *Parameter*

- *Statistic*

- *Statistic Value*

- *Observational Study*

- *Random Sampling Plan*

  - *Simple Random*

  - *Stratified*

  - *Cluster*

  - *Systematic*

- *Representative Sample*

- *Nonrandom Sampling Plan*

  - *Convenience Sample*

  - *Voluntary Response Sample*

- *Experiment (Experimental Study)*

- *Random Assignment*

- *Treatment Group*

- *Control Group*

- *Double Blind*

- *Single Blind*

➢ *Placebo*

➢ *Placebo Effect*

➢ *Predictable Behavior*

➢ *Probability*

➢ *Confidence*

➢ *Confidence Level*

➢ *Margin of Error*

➢ *Confidence Interval*

➢ *Majority*

➢ *Confidence Statement*

➢ *Statistically Significant*

➢ *Level of Significance*

➢ *p-Value*

➢ *Null and Alternative Hypotheses*

➢ *Practically or Substantively Important*

➢ **Do you know:**

- The required language for all interpretations: confidence statement, *p*-value, significance, and conclusion in hypothesis test?

- The rules we use to determine when results are statistically significant and not statistically significant?

➢ **Can you:**

- Clearly describe the individual, variable, population, sample, parameter, and statistic in context, when given a brief study description?

- Identify a sampling plan from a description?

- Identify which sampling plans are random and nonrandom?

- Distinguish between observational and experimental studies from brief descriptions?

- Explain why a study is observational or experimental?

- Describe the treatment and control groups for an experiment when given a study description?

- Determine and explain blinding in an experiment when given a study description?

- Find the estimated 95% margin of error and find the confidence interval?

- Write a complete confidence statement?

- Determine and explain if a confidence interval suggests a majority of the population feels a certain way?

- Provide the complete *p*-value explanation, determine and explain statistical significance, provide the complete conclusion, and respond to relevant questions when provided a brief description of hypothesis test results?

EXERCISES

The leading causes of death among young people in the United States, aged 10 to 24 years, are those related to the risky behaviors of the individuals themselves. To monitor priority health behaviors, the prevalence of obesity, overweight and asthma, and other priority health behaviors among youth and young adults, Centers for Disease Control and Prevention (CDC) developed the Youth Risk Behavior Surveillance System (YRBSS). YRBSS includes school-based national, state, and large urban school district Youth Risk Behavior Surveys (YRBS) conducted among representative samples of students in grades 9–12. National, state, and large urban school district surveys have been conducted biennially since 1991. The national survey is conducted in both public and private schools, however, high school-age individuals who do not attend school are not represented in the sample. Students from all 50 states and the District of Columbia are included.

The national YRBS sample is designed to produce estimates that are accurate within ±5% at a 95% confidence level. Overall estimates as well as estimates for sex, grade, race/ethnicity, grade by sex, and race/ethnicity by sex subgroups meet this standard. Estimates for grade by race/ethnicity subgroups are accurate within ±5% at a 90% confidence level. http://www.cdc.gov/healthyyouth/data/yrbs/pdf/2015/ss6506_updated.pdf

1) The 2015 YRBSS reported that during the 30 days before the survey, 20.0% of students nationwide had ridden in a car, or other vehicle, one or more times with a driver who had been drinking alcohol. Remember that the statistic and parameter descriptions contain no numerical information. Be careful on a through c, as they change slightly from one problem to the next!

   a) An individual will be:

   b) The population will be:

   c) The sample will be:

   d) Describe the statistic.

e) What is the statistic value?

f) Describe the parameter associated with the reported information.

g) Write the complete confidence statement.

2) The 2015 YRBSS reported that 50.9% of 12th-grade students had ever used electronic vapor products. Remember that the statistic and parameter descriptions contain no numerical information. Be careful on a through c, as they change slightly from one problem to the next!

a) An individual will be:

b) The population will be:

c) The sample will be:

d) Describe the statistic.

e) What is the statistic value?

f) Describe the parameter associated with the reported information.

g) Write the complete confidence statement.

h) Is it reasonable to conclude that more than a majority of 12th-grade students have used vapor products? Explain.

3) The 2015 YRBSS reported that during the 30 days before the survey, 61.9% of 12th-grade males had texted or e-mailed while driving. Remember that the statistic and parameter descriptions contain no numerical information. Be careful on a through c, as they change slightly from one problem to the next! The confidence level changes on this one!

a) An individual will be:

b) The population will be:

c) The sample will be:

d) Describe the statistic.

e) What is the statistic value?

f) Describe the parameter associated with the reported information.

g) Write the complete confidence statement.

h) Is it reasonable to conclude that more than a majority of 12th-grade males have texted or e-mailed while driving? Explain.

4) Gallup poll about the environment in March 2016. They initially contacted over 2000 individuals by land and cell phones, but the results are based on the opinions of 1,019 randomly selected US adults. Fifty-one percent of these respondents said they opposed "fracking" as a means of increasing the production of natural gas and oil in the United States. Remember that the statistic and parameter descriptions contain no numerical information (http://www.gallup.com).

a) An individual will be:

b) The population will be:

c) The sample will be:

d) Describe the statistic.

e) What is the statistic value?

f) Describe the parameter associated with the reported information.

g) What is the approximate margin of error? (Show the calculation and keep two decimal places for the percentage form.)

h) Write the complete confidence statement.

i) Is it reasonable to conclude that more than a majority of US adults are opposed "fracking" as a means of increasing the production of natural gas and oil in the United States? Explain.

5) What kind of sampling does each description illustrate?

a) Frances is interested in whether students at his college would like to see a portion of the campus preserved as green space. He leaves surveys at the door of each dorm room on campus and asks students to return completed surveys to a box he leaves at the front door of each dorm. He will analyze the surveys of the students that return them to those boxes.

b) Frances is interested in whether students at his college would like to see a portion of the campus preserved as green space. He assigns each floor of every dorm with a code and then uses those codes to randomly select six floors. He then obtains responses from every student living on those floors.

c) Frances is interested in whether students at his college would like to see a portion of the campus preserved as green space. He goes out on the quad on a sunny day, then asks and receives a response from the first 100 students that he sees.

6) What kind of sampling does each description illustrate?

   a) Suppose lawmakers are interested in finding out whether a newly instituted elementary school program about bullying is effective. The United States has long considered the country to have four distinct census regions: Northeast, Midwest, South, and West. A government statistician randomly selects a sample of 30 elementary schools from each region. Representatives from each of those schools will be interviewed and surveyed regularly for two years.

   b) Suppose state lawmakers are interested in finding out whether a newly instituted elementary school program about bullying is effective. A statistician gets a numbered list of all elementary schools in the state and has a computer program randomly select 25 numbers. The 25 elementary schools with corresponding numbers will be the sample. Representatives from each of those schools will be interviewed and surveyed regularly for two years.

7) A marketing company claims that the mean household income of HDTV owners across the United States is greater than $50,000. A random sample of 1,700 households with HDTVs shows has a mean household income of $51,182. Assuming the true mean household income is $50,000, the probability of selecting a sample with a mean income of $51,182 or more is 0.007. Does it appear the marketing company is correct?

   H_0: The true mean household income of US households with HDTVs is $50,000.

   H_a: The true mean household income of US households with HDTVs is greater than $50,000.

   Outline the decision process by completing the four bolded items.

   a) *p-value explanation:*

b) *Statistical significance determination and reason:*

c) *Conclusion:*

d) *Respond to the question:*

8) Some say that duct tape can fix anything, but when researchers announced that duct tape may be a more effective and less painful alternative to liquid nitrogen in removing warts, many were skeptical. A 2002 article described a study at Madigan Army Medical Center to test the effectiveness of duct tape as a treatment for warts. Researchers randomly assigned patients with warts, age 3 to 22 years, to either a duct tape treatment or to the more traditional liquid nitrogen freezing treatment. Those in the duct tape group wore duct tape for six days, then removed the tape, soaked the area in water, and used an emery board to scrape the area. The liquid nitrogen treatment involves in-office freezing of the wart with liquid nitrogen for 10 to 20 seconds every two to three weeks and often results in pain and other uncomfortable complications. Both procedures were repeated for two months or until the wart disappeared. http://www.ncbi.nlm.nih.gov/pubmed/12361440/

a) The sample is:

b) The treatment group is:

c) The control group is:

At the end of the study, it was reported that 60% patients using the liquid nitrogen saw their warts removed and that 85% of the patients using duct tape saw their warts removed. The probability of observing a difference in the samples' cure rates at least as extreme as that observed in the study was 0.0000. Can we conclude that duct tape is a more effective treatment for curing warts than liquid nitrogen?

H_o: *The percentage of wart patients that will be cured of their warts is the same with duct tape treatment and liquid nitrogen treatment.*

H_a: *The percentage of wart patients that will be cured of their warts is higher with duct tape treatment than with liquid nitrogen treatment.*

Outline the decision process by completing the four bolded items.

d) *p-value explanation:*

e) *Statistical significance determination and reason:*

f) *Conclusion:*

g) *Respond to the question:*

9) In March 2007, the results of another study about duct tape as a treatment for warts was published in JAMA Dermatology. This study, conducted at Minneapolis Veterans Affairs Medical Center, used wart patients with a median age of 54 years. The patients were randomly assigned to receive a duct tape treatment or moleskin treatment. Both treatments' pads were disguised to appear identical and provided to the patients. Patients were instructed to wear a single pad for seven days, remove the pad on the evening of day 7, and use nothing on the wart overnight. The morning of day 8, patients soaked and scraped the wart with a coarse-grit emery board and then applied a new pad. This was repeated for the entire two-monthtreatmentperiod.http://archderm.jamanetwork.com/article.aspx?articleid=411864

a) The sample is:

b) The treatment group is:

c) The control group is:

At the end of this study, 21% of the duct tape group had been cured and 22% of the moleskin group had been cured. The probability of observing a difference in the samples' cure rates as extreme as that observed in the two groups was 0.99. Can we conclude that duct tape is a more effective treatment for curing warts than moleskin?

H_o: *The percentage of wart patients that will be cured of their warts is the same with duct tape treatment and moleskin treatment.*

H_a: *The percentage of wart patients that will be cured of their warts is higher with duct tape treatment than with moleskin treatment.*

Outline the decision process by completing the four bolded items.

d) *p-value explanation:*

e) *Statistical significance determination and reason:*

f) *Conclusion:*

g) *Respond to the question:*

h) *In this study, the moleskin was the placebo treatment and never expected to be an effective treatment. But what are some potential reasons for the poor duct tape outcomes?*

CHAPTER 6
Working with Set and Categorical Variable Relationships

CHAPTER OBJECTIVES

Upon completion of this chapter, the student should be able to

- ❑ Write verbal descriptions of each region of Venn diagram involving two or three sets, when the Venn diagram and brief description is provided.
- ❑ When provided a verbal description of the relationship between two or three sets, create the Venn diagram and/or report the number of elements in each region of the diagram.
- ❑ Respond to numerical questions based on two and three set Venn diagrams.
- ❑ Determine probabilities from a two-way table when the status of either one or both categorical variables is unknown.
- ❑ Create a two-way table when given rates for prevalence, sensitivity, and specificity.

Often, it is important in mathematics and statistics to understand and describe relationships between sets (or variables) and to adjust needed calculations based on them. To organize, visualize, and then facilitate calculations of these relationships, we use two basic tools: Venn diagrams and two-way tables.

6.1 VENN DIAGRAMS—SET BASICS

A discussion of Venn diagrams requires that we first define some basic "set" terminology.

> ➢ A **set** is a collection of objects.
> ➢ The objects that make up a set are called **elements** or **members**.
> ➢ The collection of all objects being considered is called the **universe** or **universal set**.

6.1.1 Venn Diagrams as Tools That Help Us "See" Relationships between Sets

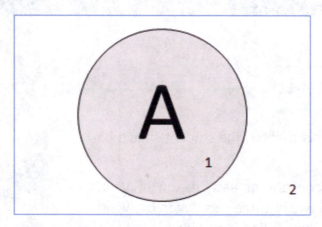

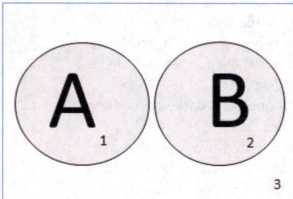

As shown in the top Venn diagram, the rectangle represents the universe. The shaded circle represents a set called "A."

The white space outside set A but inside the rectangle contains all the elements in the universe that are not in set A, **the complement of A**.

Though only one set is designated in this universe, note that there are **two regions** (*Numbered 1 and 2*).

The bottom Venn diagram shows that two sets, set A and set B, are defined in the universe.

Sets A and B have no elements in common and are said to be **disjoint**.

The elements that are not in set A include the elements in the white space as well as the elements of set B.

The elements that are not in set B include the elements in the white space as well as the elements of set A.

There are three regions (*Numbered 1, 2, and 3*).

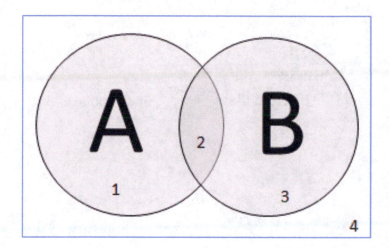

The Venn diagram above once again shows two sets, set A and set B, but this time the sets overlap or **intersect**.

The elements not in set A include the elements in the white space as well as the elements of B that are not in the overlap region.

The elements not in set B include the elements in the white space and the elements of A that are not in the overlap region.

There are four regions (*Numbered 1, 2, 3, and 4 for illustration*).

Region 2, where the two sets overlap, is made up of the elements that are in **both** set A **AND** set B.

The elements in set A **OR** set B include the elements in regions 1, 2, and 3. *NOTE that the elements of set A **OR** set B include what they have in common.*

EXAMPLE 1: Though we rarely work at the element level, an example at that level can help us understand the basic set relationships. So, let the universe be the objects in a teacher's office. For illustration purposes, this teacher's office has amazingly few items.

U = {desk, chair, table, computer, stapler, graded papers, pens, textbook, calculator}

Several sets might be defined for this universe. Here are two:

Set of items taken to class = {graded papers, pens, textbook, calculator}

Set of technological tools = {computer, calculator}

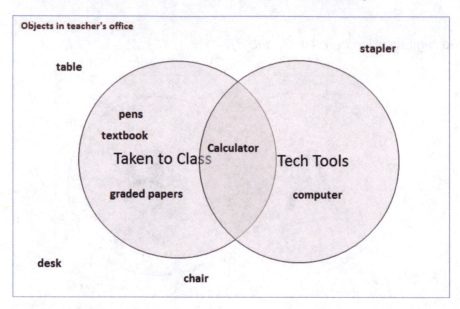

a) List the objects from the teacher's office that are either *taken to class* **OR** are *tech tools*.

Computer, graded papers, pens, textbook, calculator

b) List the objects from the teacher's office that are *taken to class* **AND** are *tech tools*?

Calculator

c) List the objects from the teacher's office that are **not** *taken to class*?

Desk, chair, table, computer, stapler

d) List the objects from the teacher's office that are **not** *tech tools*?

Desk, chair, table, stapler, graded papers, pens, textbook

e) List the objects from the teacher's office that are **not** *taken to class* **AND** are **not** *tech tools*?

Desk, chair, table, stapler

f) List the objects from the teacher's office that are **not** *taken to class* **OR** are **not** *tech tools*?

Desk, chair, table, computer, stapler, graded papers, pens, textbook

6.1.2 Describe the Regions of a Venn Diagram

Starting with the information from the previous example, *the universe is all the objects in the teacher's office*. We have defined two sets: *items that are taken to class* and *technological tools*. The basic Venn diagram for the situation is shown below but this time without the detail of the individual elements. Each of the four regions has now been labelled with a number.

EXAMPLE 2: Describe each of the four regions in terms of both sets:

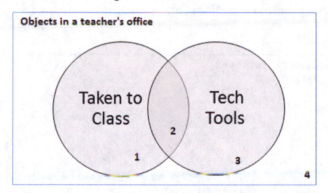

Region 1 includes objects in the teacher's office that are taken to class but are not technological tools.

Region 2 includes objects in the teacher's office that are taken to class and are technological tools.

Region 3 includes objects in the teacher's office that are technological tools but not taken to class.

Region 4 includes objects in the teacher's office that are not taken to class and are not technological tools.

6.1.3 Determine the Number of Elements in Each Region

EXAMPLE 3: Now consider a numerical problem based on the Venn diagram shown above. Suppose the following:

➤ There are 20 objects in the teacher's office (each set of graded papers or set of pens is considered 1 object).
➤ The teacher has three technological tools that are taken to class and one desktop computer.
➤ The total number of objects that she takes to class is 10.

How many elements are in each region?

➢ We are told that there are three technological tools that are taken to class, so *region 2 has three elements*.
➢ There are 10 objects taken to class, but three of those are the tech tools in region 2, so *region 1 has seven elements*.
➢ Although she has four technological tools, three are in region 2, *so region 3 has one element*.
➢ The number of elements in region 4 is whatever remains, 20 − (3 + 7 + 1) = 9, so *region 4 has nine elements*.

The Venn diagram below shows the number of objects in each region, which allows us to easily answer questions like those below the diagram.

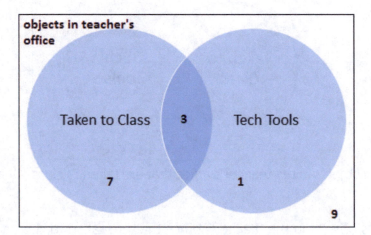

How many of the teacher's objects were either taken to class or were tech tools?

7 + 3 + 1 = 11

How many of the teacher's objects were not taken to class?

1 + 9 = 10

YOUR TURN 2: Answer the questions, showing any necessary calculations.

a) How many objects are tech tools or not taken to class?

b) How many objects are tech tools and not taken to class?

6.1.4 Working with Three-Set Venn Diagrams

All the explanations and tools learned in the examples for two-set Venn diagrams also apply when three sets are defined. We will work with overlapping sets with a Venn diagram similar to the one shown in the examples that follow.

EXAMPLE 4: *Describe the regions of the Venn diagram in terms of all three sets*: The universe includes all students at a school. Set M represents students taking math. Set B represents students taking biology. Set H represents students taking history. With three overlapping sets, there are eight regions to describe (numbered one through eight on the Venn diagram). Each description must address all three sets.

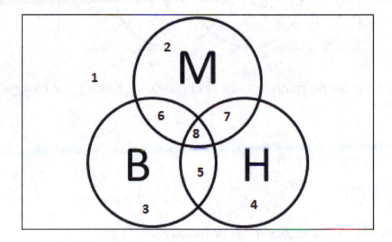

Region 1 includes students who are not taking math and not taking history and not taking biology.

Region 2 includes students who are taking math but are taking neither history nor biology. (It could also be described as students who are taking math but are not taking history and not taking biology.)

Region 3 includes students who are taking biology but taking neither math nor history.

Region 4 includes students who are taking history but taking neither math nor biology.

Region 5 includes students taking both biology and history but not taking math.

Region 6 includes students taking both biology and math but not taking history.

Region 7 includes students taking both math and history but not taking biology.

Region 8 includes students taking math, history, and biology.

EXAMPLE 5: *Answer numerical questions when region values are specified*: Start with the same universe and same sets of **Example 4**. The numbers shown in each region of the Venn diagram represent the number of students in that region. Use the Venn diagram to respond to the questions that follow.

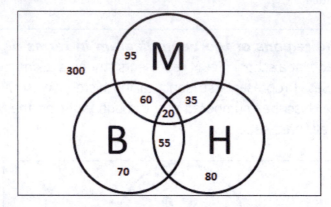

How many students are taking math but are taking neither history nor biology?

95

How many students are taking math?

95 + 60 + 20 + 35 = 210

How many students are taking either math or biology?

70 + 55 + 20 + 60 + 95 + 35 = 335

How many students are taking either math or biology but not taking history?

70 + 60 + 95 = 225

YOUR TURN 3: Answer the questions, showing any necessary calculations.

a) How many students are taking biology but not math?

b) How many students are not taking math?

c) How many students are represented?

QUANTITATIVE LITERACY AND REASONING

EXAMPLE 6: *Determine the number of elements in eight regions and answer numerical questions when region values are specified*: It was once said that country western songs emphasize three basic themes: people in love (L), people in prison (P), and people who drive trucks (T). A survey of songs played on a country western radio station produced the following data on the song themes:

12 songs about a truck driver who is in love while in prison

28 songs about someone in love

13 songs about a prisoner in love

18 songs about a truck driver in love

30 songs about truck drivers

3 songs about a truck driver in prison who is not in love

2 songs about someone in prison who is not in love and not a truck driver

8 songs about someone not in prison who is not in love and not a truck driver

Use the information from the survey to fill in the number of songs in each of the eight regions of the Venn diagram shown below.

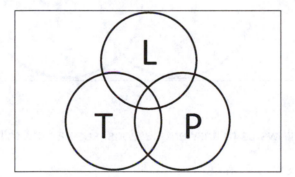

HINTS: Start with the innermost region and work outward. Look first at the survey information descriptions that mention all three sets. *This time they are shaded in the descriptions above.*

Once you fill in those four values, your Venn diagram should look as follows.

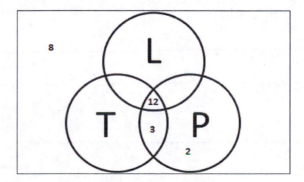

Continuing to the remaining regions, we are told 13 songs are about prisoners in love but 12 of those were already counted in the center: 13 − 12 = 1

Eighteen songs are about truck drivers in love, but again 12 were already counted: 18 − 12 = 6

There are 30 truck driver songs but many of those were already counted: 30 − 6 − 12 − 3 = 9

There were 28 songs about love but again many were previously counted: 28 − 6 − 12 − 1 = 9

Once you add these four final calculations to the diagram, it should look like completed diagram shown below. This allows us to answer questions, such as the following:

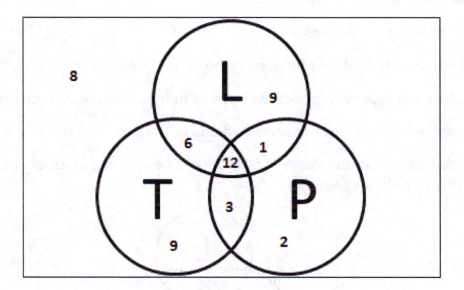

The completed diagram allows us to answer questions, such as the following:

How many songs were about prisoners?

2 + 3 + 12 + 1 = 18

How many songs are represented?

8 + 9 + 1 + 12 + 6 + 9 + 3 + 2 = 50

How many songs were not about love?

50 − (9 + 1 + 12 + 6) = 22 **OR**

9 + 8 + 3 + 2 = 22

a) How many songs were about love or prisoners?

b) How many songs were about love and prisoners?

c) How many songs were about love and prisoners but not truck drivers?

6.2 TWO-WAY TABLES

Two-way tables are great tools for organizing information when two categorical variables are used to categorize each response, object, or individual. They are particularly helpful when we need to calculate probabilities that take both variables into consideration.

Two-way tables can help us understand many common real-life situations like the results of a medical test. As lay people, most of us tend to think of medical testing in absolute terms, if the medical test is positive then it means we have the disease, if the medical test is negative then we do not have the disease. Unfortunately, medical tests are rarely 100% accurate. Most approved medical tests have high rates of correctly giving positive results for "infected" samples and negative results for "noninfected" samples but most can also result in false positives and false negatives. In situations where the vast majority of the tested samples are not infected, the number of false positives can be very high.

The table below represents 100,000 hypothetical samples tested for HIV. It shows two categorical variables: actual HIV status (has HIV/no HIV) and HIV test result (positive for HIV/negative for HIV).

		Actual HIV Status of Sample		
		Has HIV	No HIV	Total
HIV test result	Positive for HIV	594	994	1,588
	Negative for HIV	6	98,406	98,412
	Total	600	99,400	100,000

The values from this table will be used throughout this section to calculate probabilities in the examples and Your Turn problems. (Keep at least four decimal places, except when the probability terminates prior to that.)

Note that the relationships expressed in the table above correspond to the Venn diagram below. Though probabilities could be calculated directly from the Venn diagram information, the inclusion of column and row totals on the two-way table makes those calculations much easier.

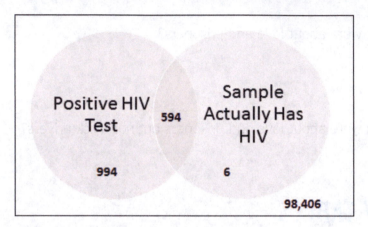

6.2.1 Calculating Probabilities Based on Two-Way Tables

EXAMPLE 7a: If one sample is selected at random from these samples, what is the probability that the sample has HIV?

Note how the question is expressed mathematically using $P(\underline{\hspace{1cm}})$ labelling, which is read as "the probability of" whatever is stated inside the parentheses.

$$P(sample\ has\ HIV) = \frac{number\ of\ samples\ with\ HIV}{total\ number\ of\ samples} = \frac{600}{100,000} = 0.006$$

This numerical outcome represents the rate of HIV in this population. The rate of disease in the population is called the **prevalence**. So, in this population, the prevalence (in percent form) is 0.6%.

EXAMPLE 7b: If one sample is selected at random from these samples, what is the probability that the sample has a positive test result?

$$P(sample\ has\ a\ positive\ test\ result) = \frac{number\ of\ samples\ with\ positive\ test\ results}{total\ number\ of\ samples} = \frac{1,588}{100,000}$$

$$\approx 0.0159$$

YOUR TURN 5a: If one sample is selected at random from these samples, what is the probability that the sample actually does not have HIV?

$$P(\text{sample does not have HIV}) = \frac{\text{number of samples that do not have HIV}}{\text{total number of samples}} = \frac{}{100,000} =$$

YOUR TURN 5b: If one sample is selected at random from these samples, what is the probability that the sample has a negative test result?

$$P(\text{sample has } \underline{\hspace{6cm}})$$

$$= \frac{\text{number of samples with } \underline{\hspace{3cm}} \text{ test results}}{\text{total number of samples}} = \frac{}{100,000} =$$

EXAMPLE 8: If one sample is selected at random from these samples, what is the probability that the sample is one that had a positive test result and has HIV?

$$P(\text{positive test result and has HIV}) = \frac{\text{number of samples with positive results and HIV}}{\text{total number of samples}}$$

$$= \frac{594}{100,000} \approx 0.0059$$

YOUR TURN 6: If one sample is selected at random from these samples, what is the probability that the sample is one that had a negative test result and does not have HIV?

$$P(\underline{\hspace{4cm}} \text{ and } \underline{\hspace{3cm}}) =$$

$$\frac{\text{number of samples with } \underline{\hspace{2cm}} \text{ results and } \underline{\hspace{2cm}}}{\text{total number of samples}} = \hspace{2cm} =$$

Now look at the probabilities when either the HIV status or the actual test result is already known.

EXAMPLE 9: If one sample is selected at random from those known to have HIV, what is the probability that the HIV test result was positive?

Note that the more complex scenario requires changes to the labelling to reflect that one categorical variable's status is known. The notation before the equal sign is read "**the probability of** a positive test result **given that** the sample has HIV." So, the "|" is read as "given that."

$$P(\text{positive test result} \mid \text{sample has HIV})$$

$$= \frac{number\ of\ positive\ test\ results\ for\ samples\ with\ HIV}{number\ of\ samples\ with\ HIV} = \frac{594}{600} = 0.99$$

In a medical test, the **sensitivity** of the test is the percentage of diseased samples that will test positive for the disease. *So, for this HIV test, the sensitivity is 99%.*

Caution: The "given that" notation is **NOT** expressing a fraction!

$$P\,(positive\ test\ result\ |\ sample\ has\ HIV)\ is\ not\ P\left(\frac{positive\ test\ result}{sample\ has\ HIV}\right).$$

YOUR TURN 7: If one sample is selected at random from those known to not have HIV, what is the probability that the HIV test result was negative?

$$P\,(negative\ test\ result\ |\ sample\ does\ not\ have\ HIV)$$

$$= \frac{number\ of\ negative\ test\ results\ for\ samples\ without\ HIV}{number\ of\ samples\ without\ HIV} = \frac{}{99,400} =$$

In a medical test, the **specificity** of the test is the percentage of nondiseased samples that will test negative for the disease. *For this HIV test the specificity is 99%, which happens to be the same rate as the sensitivity. THIS IS NOT ALWAYS THE CASE. The sensitivity and specificity of medical tests are often different values!*

It seems obvious that this a pretty accurate test, correct? If we happen to know the HIV status of samples in advance of the test, this test clearly tends to correctly reflect that status the vast majority of the time. BUT since we typically take medical tests to diagnose a disease, how often would you <u>know</u> the disease status in advance of taking the test? So, it is important that we now look at what happens when we only know the test result, as would typically be the case in a clinical setting.

EXAMPLE 10a: If one sample is selected at random from those with a positive test result, what is the probability that the sample actually has HIV?

$$P\,(sample\ has\ HIV\ |\ test\ result\ was\ positive)$$

$$= \frac{number\ of\ positive\ test\ results\ for\ samples\ with\ HIV}{number\ of\ positive\ test\ results} = \frac{594}{1,588} \approx 0.3741$$

Stop and think about this outcome for a moment. *This is telling us that, in this population, only about 37.41% of the positive test results are actually for samples with HIV.*

EXAMPLE 10b: If one sample is selected at random from those with a positive test result, what is the probability that the sample actually does not have HIV?

$$P(\text{sample has no HIV} \mid \text{test result was positive})$$

$$= \frac{\text{number of positive test results for samples without HIV}}{\text{number of positive test results}} = \frac{994}{1,588}$$

$$\approx 0.6278$$

YOUR TURN 8a: If one sample is selected at random from those with a negative test result, what is the probability that the sample actually does not have HIV?

$$P(\text{sample does not have HIV} \mid \text{test result was negative})$$

$$= \frac{\text{number of negative test results for samples without HIV}}{\text{number of negative test results}} = \qquad =$$

YOUR TURN 8b: If one sample is selected at random from those with a negative test result, what is the probability that the sample actually has HIV?

$$P(\text{sample has HIV} \mid \text{test result was negative})$$

$$= \frac{\text{number of negative test results for samples with HIV}}{\text{number of negative test results}} = \qquad =$$

6.2.2 Creating the Two-Way Table

EXAMPLE 11: Perhaps, you are wondering about the validity of the numbers in the table, and that is certainly a legitimate concern. There are many HIV tests and the test represented here is for a cheap and fast response enzyme-linked immunosorbent assay (ELISA) test such as might be used initially in diagnostic testing. Though the sensitivity and specificity rates vary by brand, the 99% rates used here are comparable to existing tests. *Cheap and fast are both critical characteristics in a clinical setting for diseases such as HIV because test cost and effectiveness means more people will get tested and fast turnaround means the patients get initial results in one visit.* The 0.6% prevalence is in the middle of the interval stated by the US Centers for Disease Control and Prevention (CDC) and UN (www.unaids.org) for the estimated prevalence within the US adult population.

The table used earlier was derived mathematically using the information stated in the previous paragraph. We start with a hypothetical population of size 100,000 with the 0.6% HIV prevalence and an HIV test with sensitivity and specificity of 99%. You can arrive at the table values following the steps listed below the table. Note that the step order is indicated on the table with the numbers one through nine on the right side of the cells.

| | | Actual HIV Status of Sample | | |
		Has HIV	No HIV	Total
HIV test result	Positive for HIV	594	994	1,588
	Negative for HIV	6	98,406	98,412
	Total	600	99,400	100,000

1) Enter the size of the hypothetical population: 100,000

2) To find number with HIV:

   *Multiply the **prevalence** in decimal form by the population size*: 0.006(100,000) = 600

3) To find number without HIV, subtract as follows:

   Population size − Number with HIV: 100,000 − 600 = 99,400

4) To find number with HIV that are correctly get a positive test result:

   *Multiply the number with HIV by **sensitivity** in decimal form*: 600(0.99) = 594

5) To find the number with HIV that will incorrectly get a negative test result, subtract as follows:

   Number with HIV − Number correctly receiving positive test result = 600 − 594 = 6

6) To find number without HIV that will correctly receive a negative test result:

   *Multiply Number without HIV by **specificity** in decimal form*: 99,400 (0.99) = 98,406

7) To find the number of those without HIV that will incorrectly receive a positive test result, subtract:

   Number without HIV − Number of correct negative results: 99,400 − 98,406 = 994

8) *Add across to get total number of positive test results*: 594 + 994 = 1,588

9) *Add across to get total number of negative test results*: 6 + 98,406 = 98,412

   Be sure that you always verify that all table entries are accurate, including all row and column totals, before beginning any probability calculations!

YOUR TURN 9: Start with a hypothetical population size of 100,000. Then assume a 0.9% HIV prevalence and an HIV test with sensitivity and specificity of 99%. Use this information to complete the table.

		Actual HIV Status of Sample		
		Has HIV	**No HIV**	**Total**
HIV test result	Positive for HIV			
	Negative for HIV			
	Total			100,000

YOUR TURN ANSWERS

1) graded papers, pens, textbook

2) a) 13   b) 1

3) a) 125   b) 505   c) 715

4) a) 33   b) 13   c) 1

5) a) 99,400; 0.994   b) negative test, negative, 98,412; 0.98412

6) negative test, no HIV, negative test, No HIV, $\dfrac{98,406}{100,000}$; 0.98406

7) 98,406; 0.99

8) a) $\dfrac{98,406}{98,412}$; 0.9999   b) $\dfrac{6}{98,412}$; 0.0001

9)

		Actual HIV Status of Sample		
		Has HIV	**No HIV**	**Total**
HIV test result	Positive for HIV	891	991	1,882
	Negative for HIV	9	98,109	98,118
	Total	900	99,100	100,000

CHECK YOUR MASTERY

➢ **Chapter Terminology:** *If you do not know the meaning, record it here.*

Set

Element

Universe

Complement

Disjoint

Region

Intersect

Prevalence

Sensitivity

Specificity

➢ **Can you**

- Describe the regions in terms of both sets in a two-set Venn diagram?

- Determine the number of elements in each region of a two-set Venn diagram from verbal descriptions?

- Answer numerical questions when region values of a two-set Venn diagram are specified?

- Describe the regions in terms of both sets in a three-set Venn diagram?

- Determine the number of elements in each region of a three-set Venn diagram from verbal descriptions?

- Answer numerical questions when region values of a three-set Venn diagram are specified?

- Use appropriate probability notation (in situations both with and without "given that")?

- Determine probabilities from a provided two-way table when the status of both categorical variables is unknown?

- Determine probabilities from a provided two-way table when the status of one categorical variable is known?

- Create an appropriate two-way table when given rates for prevalence, sensitivity, and specificity?

EXERCISES

1) A physician believes he has come up with a great new headache treatment. From among his patients, he and his staff chose and convinced 100 of his patients with long histories of difficult-to-treat headaches to participate in a small initial study. One group of 50 patients took his new treatment as soon as they noticed their headache, whereas the second group of 50 patients took a standard dose of ibuprofen at the first sign of a headache. The patients were provided with all study medications that were identical in every way except for the active ingredients and each kept a diary of symptoms, improvement times, and time required for the headache to disappear completely. Thirty of the patients in the treatment group consistently showed timely recovery from their headaches. Eighteen of the patients in the control group showed similar results.

a) Determine the number of patients in each of the numbered regions. Write those values in the relevant region.

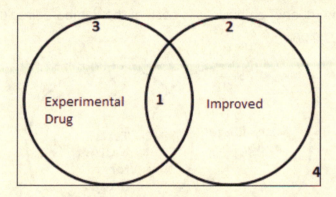

b) Completely describe in words the specified numbered regions **in terms of both sets** (use the labeling numbers shown on the Venn diagram).

Region 1 description:

Region 2 description:

Region 3 description:

Region 4 description:

---

c) How many patients improved?

d) How many patients did not improve?

e) How many patients took the experimental drug or did not improve?

f) How many patients took the ibuprofen or did not improve?

2) A company's 2,000 employees are required to take periodic drug tests as a condition of their continued employment. One hundred employees use some form of illegal drugs. Ninety of the illegal drug users test positive for drugs. One hundred ninety of the nonusers tested positive.

a) Determine the number of employees in each of the numbered regions. Write those values in the relevant region.

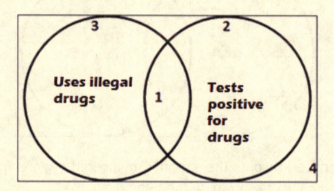

b) Completely describe in words the specified numbered regions **in terms of both sets** (use the labeling numbers shown on the Venn diagram).

Region 1 description:

Region 2 description:

Region 3 description:

Region 4 description:

e) How many employees tested positive?

f) How many employees tested negative and were not drug users?

g) What percentage of those that tested positive did not use drugs?

h) What percentage of those that used drugs tested positive?

3) The universe for the Venn diagram is all clients receiving at least one service at a small day spa on one particular day. Set M represents the clients that got a manicure. Set F represents the clients that got a facial. Set P represents the clients that got a pedicure. Describe all eight regions (numbered one through eight on the Venn diagram). Each description must address **all three sets**, as shown in Example 4.

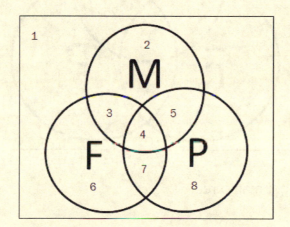

1)

2)

3)

4)

5)

6)

7)

8)

4) The universe for the Venn diagram is all clients receiving at least one service at a small day spa on one particular day. Set **M** represents the clients that got a manicure. Set **F** represents the clients that got a facial. Set **P** represents the clients that got a pedicure. The numbers shown in each region of the Venn diagram represent the number of clients in that region. Use the Venn diagram to respond to the questions that follow. Show the work of needed calculations.

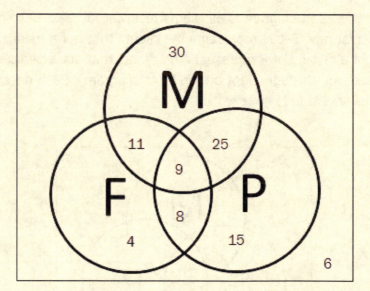

a) How many clients got manicures?

b) How many clients got manicures and pedicures?

c) How many clients got manicures and facials?

d) How many clients got manicures or pedicures?

e) How many clients got facials but not pedicures?

f) How many clients got neither manicures nor pedicures?

g) How many clients got a service other than the three listed?

h) How many clients did the spa have on that day?

i) How many clients had all three of the listed services?

j) How many clients had exactly two of the listed services?

k) How many clients had at least two of the listed services?

l) How many clients did not have a facial?

m) How many clients had exactly one of the listed services?

5) Two hundred James Madison University (JMU) students fill out a survey indicating their favorite weekend activities around the Harrisonburg area. The three top activities listed were hiking and other activities in Shenandoah National Park (NP) (S), going to JMU athletic events (A), and hanging out friends (F). Use the following information to fill in the region values for all eight regions of the Venn diagram.

75 students listed both athletic events and hanging out with friends.

90 students listed both Shenandoah NP activities and hanging out with friends.

15 students listed Shenandoah NP activities and athletic events but not hanging out with friends.

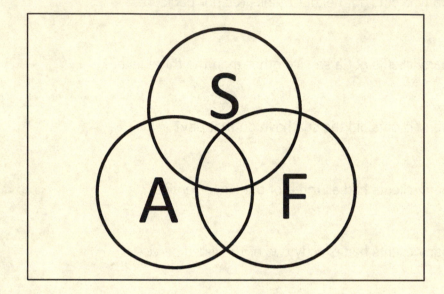

36 students listed all three top three activities.

110 students listed Shenandoah NP activities.

12 students listed only hanging with friends.

100 listed JMU athletic events.

6) Use the region values from the completed Venn diagram to answer the questions.

a) How many students that completed the survey did not list any of the top three weekend activities?

b) How many students listed athletic events or hanging out with friends?

c) How many students listed athletic events or Shenandoah NP activities?

d) How many students listed hanging out with friends?

e) How many students listed exactly two of the top three weekend activities?

f)   How many students listed at least two of the top three weekend activities?

g)   How many students listed exactly one of the top three weekend activities?

h)   How many students listed at most one of the top three weekend activities?

7) Use the table created in Your Turn 5 to answer the following. Be sure to provide the appropriate probability notation labelling, the fraction setup, and the final probability answer (to the nearest ten-thousandth if value does not terminate).

a)   If one sample is selected at random from these samples, what is the probability that the sample actually has a positive test result?

b)   If one sample is selected at random from these samples, what is the probability that the sample actually has HIV?

c)   If one sample is selected at random from these samples, what is the probability that the sample is one that had a positive test result and actually has HIV?

d)   If one sample is selected at random from those with a negative test result, what is the probability that the sample actually does not have HIV?

e) If one sample is selected at random from those known to have HIV, what is the probability that the HIV test result was positive?

f) If one sample is selected at random from those with a positive test result, what is the probability that the sample actually has HIV?

8) At one point in time, polygraph tests could be administered as a condition of consideration for employment. Laws have since been passed in the United States that prohibit such testing. After completing this problem, you will likely understand why these laws are so important.

Imagine that a company has 1,000 employees that are required to take a polygraph to keep their positions. As you can see by the column totals, most of the employees tell the truth. The sensitivity of the polygraph test for screening is 60%. (About 60% of people who are lying will be identified by the test as lying.) The specificity of the polygraph test is 90%. (About 90% of the people telling the truth will be identified by the test as telling the truth.) Use these sensitivity and specificity values to complete the table.

Polygraph test result		Actual Status of Respondent's Answer		
		Telling truth	Telling lie	
	Said truthful			
	Said lying			
		980	20	1,000

9) Use the results of the two-way table above to fill in the region values on the Venn diagram.

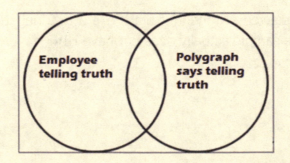

10) Use the results of the table above to answer the questions below. Be sure to provide the appropriate probability notation labelling, the fraction setup, and the final probability answer (to the nearest ten-thousandth if value does not terminate).

a) If one test result is selected at random from these 1,000 results, what is the probability that the potential employee was telling the truth?

b) If one test result is selected at random from these 1,000 results, what is the probability that the result is for a truthful test result for a truthful response?

c) If one test result is selected at random from these 1,000 results, what is the probability that the polygraph result said truthful?

d) If one test result is selected at random from those where the respondent was telling the truth, what is the probability that the polygraph said they were telling the truth?

e) If one test result is selected at random from those where the test result said truthful, what is the probability that the response was actually truthful?

f) If one test result is selected at random from those where the test result said lying, what is the probability that the response was actually truthful?

11) Use the results of the earlier polygraph two-way table to answer the questions below.

a) If one test result is selected at random from these 1,000 results, what is the probability that the potential employee was telling a lie?

b) If one test result is selected at random from these 1,000 results, what is the probability that the result is for a lying test result for a response that was a lie?

c) If one test result is selected at random from these 1,000 results, what is the probability that the polygraph result said lying?

d) If one test result is selected at random from those where the respondent was telling a lie, what is the probability that the polygraph said they were telling a lie?

e) If one test result is selected at random from those where the test result said truthful, what is the probability that the response was actually a lie?

f) If one test result is selected at random from those where the test result said lying, what is the probability that the response was actually lying?

APPENDIX I
Basic Skills Review

BASIC SKILLS REVIEW

Every college student needs to have fundamental mastery of basic arithmetic skills as well as the ability to solve simple linear and quadratic equations. This appendix briefly reviews some of the fundamental skills that were taught in your K–12 education. This text assumes you can perform these basic skills **without** the use of a calculator.

Notes on Rounding and Required Number of Decimal Places

Determining the number of decimal places to keep in recording final answers is a concern that crops up repeatedly in classes where calculations are necessary. Occasionally, rounding expectations will be spelled out as part of the problem itself and, when specified, you must follow that guidance. Otherwise the following standards for rounding are used in this book and are not restated in every problem.

➢ Except when specified otherwise, we round and record final decimal answers to the nearest ten-thousandth and, when the response is to be written in percentage form, that recorded answer is reported to the nearest hundredth.

> In the situation where the decimal form has no digits other than 0 until beyond that the ten-thousandth position, do not round to 0. Give enough digits to see the first nonzero value.
> When rounding to the nearest ten-thousandth place, you need to see at least the hundred-thousandth place. If that place is a digit of 5 or higher, then the ten-thousandth place digit will be rounded up.

I.1 BASIC TERMINOLOGY

The terms listed below are used throughout this book. Because people remember what they write themselves better than what they simply view, use the internet to find a mathematical definition of each term.

Factor

Term

Expression

Variable

Equation

I.2 FRACTION ARITHMETIC

Evaluate the following expressions, completing and showing all work in fractions. Reduce each answer completely by dividing the answer by 1 in the appropriate fraction form. Some answers will be improper fractions; do not rewrite as mixed numbers.

Basic steps: For addition and subtraction, you must have a common denominator. This is done by multiplying each term in the expression by the fractional form of 1 that will result in the needed denominator. Reduce when necessary. Leave answer as an improper fraction.

a) $\dfrac{2}{3}+\dfrac{3}{4}=\dfrac{2}{3}\left(\dfrac{4}{4}\right)+\dfrac{3}{4}\left(\dfrac{3}{3}\right)=\dfrac{8}{12}+\dfrac{9}{12}=\dfrac{17}{12}$

b) $\dfrac{2}{3}-\dfrac{3}{4}=\dfrac{2}{3}\left(\dfrac{4}{4}\right)-\dfrac{3}{4}\left(\dfrac{3}{3}\right)=\dfrac{8}{12}-\dfrac{9}{12}=-\dfrac{1}{12}$

c) $\dfrac{2}{3}-\dfrac{3}{8}=\dfrac{2}{3}\left(\dfrac{8}{8}\right)-\dfrac{3}{8}\left(\dfrac{3}{3}\right)=\dfrac{16}{24}-\dfrac{9}{24}=\dfrac{7}{24}$

d) $4\dfrac{2}{3}+-2\dfrac{1}{4}=\dfrac{14}{3}+-\dfrac{9}{4}=\dfrac{14}{3}\left(\dfrac{4}{4}\right)+-\dfrac{9}{4}\left(\dfrac{3}{3}\right)=\dfrac{56}{12}-\dfrac{27}{12}=\dfrac{29}{12}$

For multiplication, multiply numerators and multiply denominators. Reduce when necessary. Leave answer as an improper fraction.

e) $\dfrac{2}{3} \times \dfrac{3}{4} = \dfrac{2 \times 3}{3 \times 4} = \dfrac{6}{12} = \dfrac{6 \div 6}{12 \div 6} = \dfrac{1}{2}$

f) $4\dfrac{2}{3} \times -2\dfrac{1}{4} = \dfrac{14}{3} \times -\dfrac{9}{4} = -\dfrac{126}{12} = -\dfrac{126}{12} \div \dfrac{6}{6} = -\dfrac{21}{2}$

For division, invert the second fraction, then multiply numerators and multiply denominators. Reduce when necessary. Leave answer as an improper fraction.

g) $\dfrac{2}{3} \div \dfrac{3}{4} = \dfrac{2}{3} \times \dfrac{4}{3} = \dfrac{2 \times 4}{3 \times 3} = \dfrac{8}{9}$

h) $4\dfrac{1}{3} \div -2\dfrac{3}{4} = \dfrac{13}{3} \div -\dfrac{11}{4} = \dfrac{13}{3} \times -\dfrac{4}{11} = -\dfrac{52}{33}$

I.3 CHANGING NUMBER FORMS

Write the following as a common fraction, in reduced form. All work must be completed with fractions.

To go from decimal form to fraction, rewrite the decimal as a fraction with a 1 denominator, multiply numerator and denominator by the fractional form of 1 (both numerator and denominator will be the same multiple of 10) that will move the decimal in the numerator to the right of the last digit. Reduce the fraction.

a) $0.0236 = \dfrac{0.0236}{1} = \dfrac{0.0236 \times 10{,}000}{1 \times 10{,}000} = \dfrac{236 \div 4}{10{,}000 \div 4} = \dfrac{59}{2{,}500}$

To go from percentage form to fraction, rewrite percentage value as a decimal, then rewrite the decimal as a fraction with a 1 denominator, multiply numerator and denominator by the fractional form of 1 that will move the decimal in the numerator to the right of the last digit. Simplify the fraction.

b) $0.45\% = 0.0045 = \dfrac{0.0045 \times 10{,}000}{1 \times 10{,}000} = \dfrac{45 \div 5}{10{,}000 \div 5} = \dfrac{9}{2{,}000}$

Convert the fraction to decimal form by using long division; write each answer in the indicated rounded form. Rewrite each rounded decimal form in percentage form.

c) $\dfrac{15}{7}$ to nearest thousandth <u>2.143</u>   Percentage form <u>214.3%</u>

to nearest hundredth   <u>2.14</u>   Percentage form <u>214%</u>

```
       2.1428
   7)15.0000
     14
     10
      7
     30
     28
      20
      14
       60
       56
        4
```

d) $\dfrac{5}{7}$ to nearest ten-thousandth <u>0.7143</u>   Percentage form <u>71.43%</u>

to nearest thousandth   <u>0.714</u>   Percentage form <u>71.4%</u>

```
       0.71428
   7)5.00000
     49
     10
      7
     30
     28
      20
      14
       60
       56
        4
```

QUANTITATIVE LITERACY AND REASONING

I.4 VERBALIZING LARGE AND SMALL NUMBERS

A chart with a couple of examples to help you! Note that the decimal is the only "AND" in the verbal description.

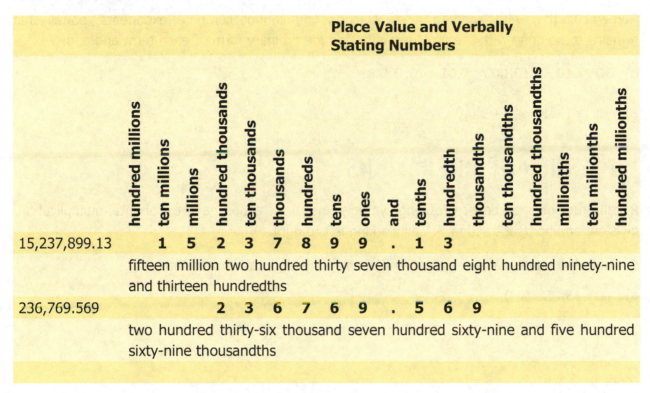

Place Value and Verbally Stating Numbers

	hundred millions	ten millions	millions	hundred thousands	ten thousands	thousands	hundreds	tens	ones	and	tenths	hundredth	thousandths	ten thousandths	hundred thousandths	millionths	ten millionths	hundred millionths
15,237,899.13	1	5	2	3	7	8	9	9	.	1	3							

fifteen million two hundred thirty seven thousand eight hundred ninety-nine and thirteen hundredths

				2	3	6	7	6	9	.	5	6	9
236,769.569				2	3	6	7	6	9	.	5	6	9

two hundred thirty-six thousand seven hundred sixty-nine and five hundred sixty-nine thousandths

Write the number value in words.

a) 5,230,000.02   five million two hundred thirty thousand and two hundredths

b) 0.000235   two hundred thirty-five millionths

c) 5,230.00002   five thousand two hundred thirty and two hundred-thousandths

I.5 EXPONENTS

Basic exponent rules:

$$a^n \times a^m = a^{n+m} \qquad \frac{a^n}{a^m} = a^{n-m} \qquad a^{-n} = \frac{1}{a^n} \qquad (a^n)^m = a^{nm} \qquad a^0 = 1$$

Evaluate the following expressions using exponent arithmetic (when possible). Give the final answers in both exponent and ordinary forms. *When exponent arithmetic is specified, the following work must be shown, not completed in your head.*

a) $10^2 \times 10^4 = 10^{2+4} = 10^6$; 1,000,000

b) $\dfrac{10^4}{10^2} = 10^{4-2} = 10^2; 100$

c) $10^2 \times 10^{-2} = 10^{2+(-2)} = 10^0 = 1$

Remember that with addition or subtraction you cannot combine exponents, so all that remains to be done with the problems is to find the ordinary form of each term and add.

d) $10^4 + 10^{-2} = 10,000 + 0.01 = 10,000.01$

e) $-3^2 + (-3)^2 = -9 + 9 = 0$

1.6 ORDER OF OPERATIONS

Recall order of operations: Grouping symbols (includes fraction bar), exponents, multiplication/division, addition/subtraction . . . all working left to right.

Evaluate the numerical expressions and simplify the algebraic expressions.

a) $-4 - 15 \div 5 \times (-3)$

$\qquad = -4 - 3 \times (-3)$

$\qquad = -4 + 9$

$\qquad = 5$

b) $\dfrac{2}{3} \times \dfrac{3}{5} - \dfrac{3}{5} \times \dfrac{3}{4}$

$\qquad = \dfrac{2 \times 3}{3 \times 5} - \dfrac{3 \times 3}{5 \times 4}$

$\qquad = \dfrac{2}{5} - \dfrac{9}{20}$

$\qquad = \dfrac{2 \times 4}{5 \times 4} - \dfrac{9}{20}$

$\qquad = \dfrac{8}{20} - \dfrac{9}{20}$

$\qquad = -\dfrac{1}{20}$

c) $\dfrac{5-3^2}{5(3-2^2)}$

$= \dfrac{5-9}{5(3-4)}$

$= \dfrac{-4}{5(-1)}$

$= \dfrac{-4}{-5}$

$= \dfrac{4}{5}$

d) $2x(2-x)-3(x-4)$

$= 4x - 2x^2 - 3x + 12$

$= -2x^2 + x + 12$

I.7 SCIENTIFIC NOTATION

Scientific notation form is $a \times 10^n$, where $1 \le a < 10$ and n is an integer. There must be exactly one digit before the decimal in a.

Write each of the following numbers in scientific notation.

a) 524.8 5.248×10^2

b) 0.0312 3.12×10^{-2}

Convert each of the following numbers from scientific to ordinary form.

c) 5.23×10^4 $52,300$

d) 2.35×10^{-4} 0.000235

Perform the indicated operations ENTIRELY in scientific notation for full credit. Give answers in scientific and ordinary notations.

e) $(3 \times 10^{-5}) \times (5 \times 10^7)$

    $= (3 \times 5) \times (10^{-5} \times 10^7)$ Regroup

    $= 15 \times 10^{-5+7}$ Simplify

$= (1.5 \times 10^1) \times 10^2$	Rewrite 15 in scientific notation form
$= 1.5 \times 10^{1+2}$	Simplify
$= 1.5 \times 10^3$	
Scientific notation 1.5×10^3	Ordinary 1,500

f) $(1 \times 10^2) \div (2 \times 10^{-4})$

$= \dfrac{1}{2} \times \dfrac{10^2}{10^{-4}}$	Regroup
$= 0.5 \times 10^{2-(-4)}$	Write fraction in decimal form; simplify expression
$= (5 \times 10^{-1}) \times 10^6$	Rewrite 0.5 in scientific notation form
$= 5 \times 10^{-1+6}$	Simplify
$= 5 \times 10^5$	
Scientific notation 5×10^5	Ordinary 500,000

1.8 BASIC FACTORING

Students have learned a variety of workable methods for factoring quadratic type expressions and it is impossible to provide all those factoring approaches here. These examples are provided to identify the types of expressions that you will be expected to factor on the assessment.

Completely factor the expressions.

a) $16x - 4x^3$

$= 4x(4 - x^2)$	Factor out common factor
$= 4x(2 - x)(2 + x)$	Factor difference of squares

b) $6x^2 - 24x$

$= 6x(x - 4)$	Factor out common factor

c) $6x^2 - 24x + 18$

$= 6(x^2 - 4x + 3)$	Factor out common factor
$= 6(x - 1)(x - 3)$	Factor quadratic expression

d) $16x + 4x^3$

$= 4x(4 + x^2)$ Factor out common factor

e) $6x^2 - 8x + 4$

$= 2(2x^2 - 4x + 2)$ Factor out common factor

$= 2(x - 1)(2x - 2)$ Factor quadratic expression

I.9 SOLVING LINEAR AND QUADRATIC EQUATIONS

Solve the following equations. Quadratic equations must be solved by factoring.

a) $16x = 4x^3$ Subtract $4x^3$ from both sides

$16x - 4x^3 = 0$

$4x(4 - x^2) = 0$ Factor out common factor

$4x(2 - x)(2 + x) = 0$ Factor difference of squares

$4x = 0$ $(2 - x) = 0$ $(2 + x) = 0$ Set each factor to 0 and solve

  $x = 0$ $-x = -2$ $x = -2$

                  $x = 2$

b) $4x^2 - 4 = 0$ Factor out common factor

$4(x - 1)(x + 1) = 0$ Factor difference of squares

$(x - 1) = 0$ $(x + 1) = 0$ Set each factor with an x to 0 and solve

    $x = 1$ $x = -1$

c) $\dfrac{2}{3}x - 2 = x - \dfrac{1}{5}$

$15\left(\dfrac{2}{3}x - 2\right) = \left(x - \dfrac{1}{5}\right)15$ Multiply by least common denominator to eliminate fractions

$$\frac{15 \times 2}{3}x - 15(2) = 15x - \frac{15}{5} \qquad \text{Simplify fractional terms}$$

$$(5 \times 2)x - 30 = 15x - 3$$

$$10x - 15x = -3 + 30 \qquad \text{Subtract } 15x \text{ and add 30 to both sides}$$

$$-5x = 27 \qquad \text{Multiply both sides by } -\frac{1}{5}$$

$$x = \frac{-27}{5}$$

CHECK YOUR MASTERY

➢ ***Do you know the appendix terminology?***

Factor

Term

Expression

Variable

Equation

➢ ***WITHOUT A CALCULATOR, can you***

- *Add, subtract, multiply, and divide fractions?*

- *Change number form from decimal to reduced fraction?*

- *Change number form from percentage to reduced fraction?*

- *Change number form from fraction to decimal using long division?*

- *Round a decimal to the nearest tenth, hundredth, thousandth, or ten-thousandth?*

- *Rewrite a decimal in percentage form?*

- *Write a number value in words?*

- *Evaluate numerical expressions using exponent arithmetic?*

- *Write an exponent expression in ordinary form?*

- *Use order of operations to evaluate numerical expressions?*

- *Use order of operations to simplify algebraic expressions?*

- *Rewrite a number in ordinary form in scientific notation?*

- *Rewrite a number in scientific notation in ordinary form?*

- *Multiply and divide numbers in scientific notation form using scientific notation arithmetic?*

- *Factor out common factors, factor differences of squares, factor quadratics?*

- *Solve linear and quadratic-type equations?*

EXERCISES

Number values used in this exercise set are purposely small for ease of calculation without a calculator. Write out all calculation steps, even those you could complete in your head, so that your instructor can see the exact work that you performed. Read and follow directions!

Evaluate the following expressions, completing and showing all work in fractions and giving final answers in <u>reduced</u> common fraction form. No mixed-number responses. Work problems vertically, with each line in the calculation equal to the previous line.

1) a) $\dfrac{4}{5} + \dfrac{3}{4}$
                                                        b) $\dfrac{4}{5} - \dfrac{3}{4}$

c) $\dfrac{4}{5} \times \dfrac{3}{4}$
                                                        d) $\dfrac{4}{5} \div \dfrac{3}{4}$

e) $3\dfrac{1}{5} \div -2\dfrac{1}{4}$
                                                        f) $3\dfrac{1}{3} \times -2\dfrac{1}{4}$

2) a) $\dfrac{4}{7} + \dfrac{2}{3}$ b) $\dfrac{4}{7} - \dfrac{2}{3}$

  c) $\dfrac{4}{7} \times \dfrac{2}{3}$ d) $\dfrac{4}{7} \div \dfrac{2}{3}$

  e) $2\dfrac{1}{3} \div -3\dfrac{1}{5}$ f) $2\dfrac{1}{3} \times -3\dfrac{1}{5}$

Write the following as a common fraction, in reduced form. All work must be completed with common fractions. No mixed-number responses. Work problems vertically, with each line in the calculation equal to the previous line.

3) a) 0.00234   b) 1.42%

c) 0.036   d) 0.034%

4) a) 0.0134   b) 2.45%

c) 0.025   d) 0.035%

Write the number value in words.

5) a) 345.0256   b) 136,789.234

6) a) 45,112,345.025

b) 36,987.20034

Convert the fraction to decimal form by using long division; round your answer to the nearest hundredth, nearest thousandth, and nearest ten-thousandth. Then, write each rounded form in percentage form. (You will have six answers to write for each problem after completing the long division.)

7) a) $\dfrac{13}{7}$

b) $\dfrac{4}{7}$

8) a) $\dfrac{12}{9}$

b) $\dfrac{8}{9}$

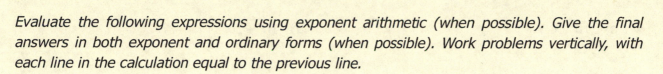

Evaluate the following expressions using exponent arithmetic (when possible). Give the final answers in both exponent and ordinary forms (when possible). Work problems vertically, with each line in the calculation equal to the previous line.

9) a) $10^6 \times 10^2$

b) $\dfrac{10^6}{10^2}$

c) $10^3 \times 10^{-3}$

d) $10^3 + 10^{-3}$

e) $-3^3 + (-3)^3$

f) $\dfrac{10^2}{10^6}$

10) a) $10^2 \times 10^3$

b) $\dfrac{10^5}{10^3}$

c) $10^4 \times 10^{-4}$

d) $10^4 + 10^{-4}$

e) $-2^3 + (-2)^3$

f) $\dfrac{10^3}{10^5}$

Evaluate the numerical expressions and simplify the algebraic expressions. All work must be completed with integers and fractions (no decimals) and final answers must be reported in __reduced__ common fraction form. No mixed-number responses. Work problems vertically, with each line in the calculation equal to the previous line.

11) a) $-5 \div 15 - 3 \times (4)$

b) $\dfrac{1}{3} \times \dfrac{2}{5} - \dfrac{3}{4} \times \dfrac{2}{3}$

c) $\dfrac{3 - 2^3}{-3(3 - 3^2)}$

d) $3x(3 - 2x) - 3(2x - 5)$

12) a) $-5+15\times3\div4$

b) $\dfrac{1}{3}\div\dfrac{2}{5}-\dfrac{3}{4}\times\dfrac{2}{3}$

c) $\dfrac{2^3-5}{3(1-3^2)}$

d) $-3x(2-5x)-3(2-x)$

Write each of the following numbers in scientific notation. Your scientific notation form must equal the original value exactly.

13) a) 345.2

b) 0.2034

14) a) 35.72

b) 0.020354

Convert each of the following numbers from scientific form to ordinary form.

15) a) 3.249×10^3 b) 5.2139×10^{-4}

16) a) 5.2409×10^5 b) 3.295×10^{-3}

Perform the indicated operations, working ENTIRELY in scientific notation to receive credit. Again, show all steps, including those that you could perform in your head. Give answers in both scientific and ordinary notations. (Converting the provided expressions into their ordinary forms and completing the calculations with those is not appropriate.) Work problems vertically, with each line in the calculation equal to the previous line.

17) a) $(4 \times 10^{-4}) \times (2 \times 10^8)$ b) $(3 \times 10^{-2}) \div (5 \times 10^2)$

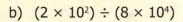

18) a) $(3 \times 10^3) \times (2 \times 10^{-5})$ b) $(2 \times 10^2) \div (8 \times 10^4)$

Completely factor the algebraic expressions. Work problems vertically, with each line in the calculation equal to the previous line.

19) a) $3x^2 - 12x$ b) $27x - 3x^3$

c) $6x^2 - 24x + 18$ d) $4x^3 - 16x$

20) a) $8x^3 - 18x$ b) $32x - 2x^3$

c) $12x^2 - x - 35$ d) $4x^4 - 16x^2$

Solve the following equations. Solve the nonlinear equations by factoring only. Work problems vertically, with each line in the calculation equal to the previous line.

21) a) $8x^3 = 18x$

b) $12x^2 - x - 35 = 0$

c) $\dfrac{2}{5}x - 2 = x - \dfrac{1}{3}$

d) $27x = 3x^3$

22) a) $6x^2 = 24x$

b) $20x^3 - 22x^2 + 6x = 0$

c) $2x - \dfrac{3}{4} = \dfrac{1}{4}x - \dfrac{1}{3}$

d) $27x^2 = 3x^3$

APPENDIX II
Standard Normal Table

STANDARD NORMAL PROBABILITIES

Table entry for **z** is the
probability lying below **z**.

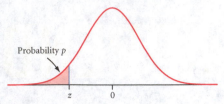

Probability *p*

z	.00	.01	.02	.03	.04	.05	.06	.07	.08	.09
−3.8	.0001	.0001	.0001	.0001	.0001	.0001	.0001	.0001	.0001	.0001
−3.7	.0001	.0001	.0001	.0001	.0001	.0001	.0001	.0001	.0001	.0001
−3.6	.0002	.0002	.0001	.0001	.0001	.0001	.0001	.0001	.0001	.0001
−3.5	.0002	.0002	.0002	.0002	.0002	.0002	.0002	.0002	.0002	.0002
−3.4	.0003	.0003	.0003	.0003	.0003	.0003	.0003	.0003	.0003	.0002
−3.3	.0005	.0005	.0005	.0004	.0004	.0004	.0004	.0004	.0004	.0003
−3.2	.0007	.0007	.0006	.0006	.0006	.0006	.0006	.0005	.0005	.0005
−3.1	.0010	.0009	.0009	.0009	.0008	.0008	.0008	.0008	.0007	.0007
−3.0	.0013	.0013	.0013	.0012	.0012	.0011	.0011	.0011	.0010	.0010
−2.9	.0019	.0018	.0018	.0017	.0016	.0016	.0015	.0015	.0014	.0014
−2.8	.0026	.0025	.0024	.0023	.0023	.0022	.0021	.0021	.0020	.0019
−2.7	.0035	.0034	.0033	.0032	.0031	.0030	.0029	.0028	.0027	.0026
−2.6	.0047	.0045	.0044	.0043	.0041	.0040	.0039	.0038	.0037	.0036
−2.5	.0062	.0060	.0059	.0057	.0055	.0054	.0052	.0051	.0049	.0048
−2.4	.0082	.0080	.0078	.0075	.0073	.0071	.0069	.0068	.0066	.0064
−2.3	.0107	.0104	.0102	.0099	.0096	.0094	.0091	.0089	.0087	.0084
−2.2	.0139	.0136	.0132	.0129	.0125	.0122	.0119	.0116	.0113	.0110
−2.1	.0179	.0174	.0170	.0166	.0162	.0158	.0154	.0150	.0146	.0143
−2.0	.0228	.0222	.0217	.0212	.0207	.0202	.0197	.0192	.0188	.0183
−1.9	.0287	.0281	.0274	.0268	.0262	.0256	.0250	.0244	.0239	.0233
−1.8	.0359	.0351	.0344	.0336	.0329	.0322	.0314	.0307	.0301	.0294
−1.7	.0446	.0436	.0427	.0418	.0409	.0401	.0392	.0384	.0375	.0367
−1.6	.0548	.0537	.0526	.0516	.0505	.0495	.0485	.0475	.0465	.0455
−1.5	.0668	.0655	.0643	.0630	.0618	.0606	.0594	.0582	.0571	.0559
−1.4	.0808	.0793	.0778	.0764	.0749	.0735	.0721	.0708	.0694	.0681
−1.3	.0968	.0951	.0934	.0918	.0901	.0885	.0869	.0853	.0838	.0823
−1.2	.1151	.1131	.1112	.1093	.1075	.1056	.1038	.1020	.1003	.0985
−1.1	.1357	.1335	.1314	.1292	.1271	.1251	.1230	.1210	.1190	.1170
−1.0	.1587	.1562	.1539	.1515	.1492	.1469	.1446	.1423	.1401	.1379
−0.9	.1841	.1814	.1788	.1762	.1736	.1711	.1685	.1660	.1635	.1611
−0.8	.2119	.2090	.2061	.2033	.2005	.1977	.1949	.1922	.1894	.1867
−0.7	.2420	.2389	.2358	.2327	.2296	.2266	.2236	.2206	.2177	.2148
−0.6	.2743	.2709	.2676	.2643	.2611	.2578	.2546	.2514	.2483	.2451
−0.5	.3085	.3050	.3015	.2981	.2946	.2912	.2877	.2843	.2810	.2776
−0.4	.3446	.3409	.3372	.3336	.3300	.3264	.3228	.3192	.3156	.3121
−0.3	.3821	.3783	.3745	.3707	.3669	.3632	.3594	.3557	.3520	.3483
−0.2	.4207	.4168	.4129	.4090	.4052	.4013	.3974	.3936	.3897	.3859
−0.1	.4602	.4562	.4522	.4483	.4443	.4404	.4364	.4325	.4286	.4247
−0.0	.5000	.4960	.4920	.4880	.4840	.4801	.4761	.4721	.4681	.4641

QUANTITATIVE LITERACY AND REASONING

STANDARD NORMAL PROBABILITIES (CONTINUED)

Table entry for **z** is the
probability lying below **z**.

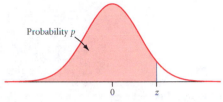

Probability *p*

z	.00	.01	.02	.03	.04	.05	.06	.07	.08	.09
0.0	.5000	.5040	.5080	.5120	.5160	.5199	.5239	.5279	.5319	.5359
0.1	.5398	.5438	.5478	.5517	.5557	.5596	.5636	.5675	.5714	.5753
0.2	.5793	.5832	.5871	.5910	.5948	.5987	.6026	.6064	.6103	.6141
0.3	.6179	.6217	.6255	.6293	.6331	.6368	.6406	.6443	.6480	.6517
0.4	.6554	.6591	.6628	.6664	.6700	.6736	.6772	.6808	.6844	.6879
0.5	.6915	.6950	.6985	.7019	.7054	.7088	.7123	.7157	.7190	.7224
0.6	.7257	.7291	.7324	.7357	.7389	.7422	.7454	.7486	.7517	.7549
0.7	.7580	.7611	.7642	.7673	.7704	.7734	.7764	.7794	.7823	.7852
0.8	.7881	.7910	.7939	.7967	.7995	.8023	.8051	.8078	.8106	.8133
0.9	.8159	.8186	.8212	.8238	.8264	.8289	.8315	.8340	.8365	.8389
1.0	.8413	.8438	.8461	.8485	.8508	.8531	.8554	.8577	.8599	.8621
1.1	.8643	.8665	.8686	.8708	.8729	.8749	.8770	.8790	.8810	.8830
1.2	.8849	.8869	.8888	.8907	.8925	.8944	.8962	.8980	.8997	.9015
1.3	.9032	.9049	.9066	.9082	.9099	.9115	.9131	.9147	.9162	.9177
1.4	.9192	.9207	.9222	.9236	.9251	.9265	.9279	.9292	.9306	.9319
1.5	.9332	.9345	.9357	.9370	.9382	.9394	.9406	.9418	.9429	.9441
1.6	.9452	.9463	.9474	.9484	.9495	.9505	.9515	.9525	.9535	.9545
1.7	.9554	.9564	.9573	.9582	.9591	.9599	.9608	.9616	.9625	.9633
1.8	.9641	.9649	.9656	.9664	.9671	.9678	.9686	.9693	.9699	.9706
1.9	.9713	.9719	.9726	.9732	.9738	.9744	.9750	.9756	.9761	.9767
2.0	.9772	.9778	.9783	.9788	.9793	.9798	.9803	.9808	.9812	.9817
2.1	.9821	.9826	.9830	.9834	.9838	.9842	.9846	.9850	.9854	.9857
2.2	.9861	.9864	.9868	.9871	.9875	.9878	.9881	.9884	.9887	.9890
2.3	.9893	.9896	.9898	.9901	.9904	.9906	.9909	.9911	.9913	.9916
2.4	.9918	.9920	.9922	.9925	.9927	.9929	.9931	.9932	.9934	.9936
2.5	.9938	.9940	.9941	.9943	.9945	.9946	.9948	.9949	.9951	.9952
2.6	.9953	.9955	.9956	.9957	.9959	.9960	.9961	.9962	.9963	.9964
2.7	.9965	.9966	.9967	.9968	.9969	.9970	.9971	.9972	.9973	.9974
2.8	.9974	.9975	.9976	.9977	.9977	.9978	.9979	.9979	.9980	.9981
2.9	.9981	.9982	.9982	.9983	.9984	.9984	.9985	.9985	.9986	.9986
3.0	.9987	.9987	.9987	.9988	.9988	.9989	.9989	.9989	.9990	.9990
3.1	.9990	.9991	.9991	.9991	.9992	.9992	.9992	.9992	.9993	.9993
3.2	.9993	.9993	.9994	.9994	.9994	.9994	.9994	.9995	.9995	.9995
3.3	.9995	.9995	.9995	.9996	.9996	.9996	.9996	.9996	.9996	.9997
3.4	.9997	.9997	.9997	.9997	.9997	.9997	.9997	.9997	.9997	.9998
3.5	.9998	.9998	.9998	.9998	.9998	.9998	.9998	.9998	.9998	.9998
3.6	.9998	.9998	.9999	.9999	.9999	.9999	.9999	.9999	.9999	.9999
3.7	.9999	.9999	.9999	.9999	.9999	.9999	.9999	.9999	.9999	.9999
3.8	.9999	.9999	.9999	.9999	.9999	.9999	.9999	.9999	.9999	.9999

INDEX